MW00804330

CURLY AND FLOPPY TWISTYTAIL

(THE FUNNY PIGGIE BOYS)

HOWARD R. GARIS

1st WORLD
LIBRARY
Literary Society

Curly and Floppy Twistytail

Howard R. Garis

© 1st World Library – Literary Society, 2004
PO Box 2211
Fairfield, IA 52556
www.1stworldlibrary.org
First Edition

LCCN: 2005906505

Softcover ISBN: 1-4218-1561-3
Hardcover ISBN: 1-4218-1461-7
eBook ISBN: 1-4218-1661-X

Purchase *"Curly and Floppy Twistytail"*
as a traditional bound book at:
www.1stWorldLibrary.org/purchase.asp?ISBN=1-4218-1561-3

1st World Library Literary Society is a nonprofit
organization dedicated to promoting literacy by:

- Creating a free internet library accessible from any
  computer worldwide.
- Hosting writing competitions and offering book
  publishing scholarships.

Curly and Floppy Twistytail
contributed by Tim, Ed & Rodney
in support of
1st World Library Literary Society

CONTENTS

STORY I

CURLY TWISTYTAIL IS NAMED

Once upon a time, not so very many years ago, in the days when there were fairies and giants and all things like that, there lived in a little house, on the edge of a wood, a family of pigs. Now these pigs weren't like the pigs, which perhaps you children have seen on most farms. No, indeed! They were just the nicest cleanest, sweetest pigs you ever dreamed of - not that pigs on a farm can't be clean, if they want to, but, somehow or other, no one seems to have time to see that they are clean. I guess it would take some one like Jennie Chipmunk to sweep and dust their pen for them.

Anyhow the pigs I am going to tell you about were very different from most pigs, and they had some very funny adventures.

First, there was the papa pig, and his name was Mr. Archibald Twistytail though no one ever called him anything but Mr. Twistytail except maybe his wife, when he forgot to bring up a scuttle of coal so she could do the washing. And then, of course there was Mrs. Twistytail - she was the mamma pig. And there were two little boy pigs, and for a time they didn't have any names, as their papa and mamma were so busy that they couldn't think what to call them. So they just said "Here sonny!" or "Hi, Bubby," whenever they wanted them to come in, or eat their dinner.

One of these little boy pigs always wore short trousers with stripes painted on them, and the other little piggie chap's trousers were like a checker-board.

And then - oh, but I almost forgot about the little baby pig. She was the sweetest little creature you can imagine, and her right name was Pinky, because she was so pink, just like a baby's toes when she sleeps in her crib. But Pinky was hardly ever called by her right name, almost every one said just "Baby," and that answered very well.

And now I'm going to tell you how one of the pigs got his name. He was the oldest pig of the three children, and one day he and his brother thought they would go out for a walk.

"Come along!" exclaimed the oldest boy pig. "Maybe we will have an adventure, such as Uncle Wiggily Longears used to have," for you see the pigs knew Uncle Wiggly almost as well as you do.

"All right," said the younger boy pig. "Where shall we go?"

"Off in the woods," spoke his brother. "The woods are full of adventures."

So they strolled out of their house, and started for the woods. I forgot to say that the Twistytail family of pigs lived in a regular house - of course not the kind you boys and girls live in, but still it was a very good house for pigs. It had tables in it, and chairs and beds and all things like that. And the reason they were called "Twistytail" was because their tails did have a sort of twist or turn in them.

Well, the two pig boys wandered on through the woods, and pretty soon they came to two paths, one leading to left and the other to the right.

"Let's go this way," said the older pig boy, who yet didn't have any name, and he pointed his leg toward the right-hand path.

"No, I think we will find an adventure on this road," said his younger brother, and he started off to the left.

"Oh, there you go!" cried the older pig boy. "You never want to do what I like!"

"Well, I've got just as good a right to go this way as you have to go that way," answered the younger piggie-iggie, and so those two brothers, instead of keeping together and looking for adventures, separated, and one went one way, while the other went the other way. And now you just wait and see what happens.

All of a sudden, as the older piggie boy was walking along, digging up nice sweet roots with his nose - for you know that is the way piggies dig - all of a sudden, I say, there was a growling noise in the bushes, and before the little pig boy could jump out of the way, or even call for his mamma or papa, a big black bear sprang out from inside a hollow stump, and grabbed him. Right in his paws he grabbed that little pig boy,

"Oh, ho!" growled the big black bear. "You are just what I've been waiting for. Now for a nice roast pork dinner. Oh, yum! yum!"

"Oh!" squealed the little pig boy. "Surely you don't mean to eat me, Mr. Bear! Please let me go!"

"Indeed I'll not!" exclaimed the bear. "I was hiding here, hoping Sammie Littletail or Uncle Wiggily would come along, so I could have a rabbit dinner, but you will do just as well. Come along!"

And so the bear carried off the little piggie boy farther into the woods, intending to take him to a den where there was a good hot fire. And all the while the little piggie tried to get away but he couldn't because the bear held him so tightly in his paws.

Pretty soon the bear came to his den. Then he said:

"Let me see, now. I must have some apple sauce to go with my roast pork dinner. I'll just tie this little pig to the fence while I go off and get some apples to make into sauce. I can cook the apples and the pig on the same fire."

Then the bear looked blinkingly at the little pig, and said:

"Let me see. How can I tie him to the fence? Oh, I know, by his tail. I'll just fasten him by his tail." And that's what he did, tying the poor little piggie to the fence by his tail, with a piece of wild grape vine for a string. And the bear wound the grape vine string, that was fast to the little pig's tail around and around the round rail of the fence. Then the bear went off after apples for sauce.

Well, of course the poor little pig felt very badly, and he didn't know what to do. He even cried a little bit, but I'm sure you won't blame him for that, will you? And he said:

"Oh, I wish my little brother was here. He might help me!"

And then, all of a sudden, there was a rustling in the bushes, and the little pig, who was tied by his tail to the fence, thought it was the bear coming back. But it wasn't, for all at once a voice called out:

"Oh, brother! What has happened to you?" And there was the piggie's little brother looking for him.

"Oh!" cried the pig boy who was tied to the fence by his tail. "A bear caught me. A big black bear! He is going to eat me as soon as he comes back with the apple sauce. Save me!"

"Indeed I will," said the little brother. And with his sharp teeth he gnawed through the grape vine string, and then his brother was free. "Come on!" exclaimed the littlest pig. "We must run home away from the bear!"

And they did, getting back to their house safely, and oh! how disappointed that bear was when he returned with the apples and found his pig dinner gone. He was so peevish that he threw all the apples away.

And when Mrs. Twistytail saw her little boy she exclaimed:

"Oh, my sakes alive! How did you get that curl in your tail?"

"I - I guess that was where the bear tied me to the fence," said the piggie boy, and so it was. His tail was all curled tight, like a little girl's hair. His mamma tried to take the curl out with a warm flatiron, but the kink stayed in the tail, and so Mr. Twistytail said:

"I guess we'll have to call our piggie boy by the name of Curly after this," and so they did, and that's how one piggie boy got the name of "Curly Twistytail."

And in case the shells don't all come off the eggs and leave the feathers sticking out for a sofa cushion, I'll tell you next how the other little pig got his name.

STORY II

FLOPPY GETS HIS NAME

One day, oh, I guess it must have been about a week after Curly Twistytail, the little pig boy, had the adventure with the bear, and his brother rescued him, as I told you in the story before this one, - one day Curly's brother, who hadn't any name as yet, said:

"Oh, Curly, let's go out for another walk, and maybe something will happen to us."

"All right," agreed Curly, "only I hope a bear doesn't happen. It's no fun to think you're going to be turned into roast pork and eaten with apple sauce," for that is what the bear was going to do, you know.

So off the two little pig brothers started, and their mamma called after them:

"Now, stay together. Don't go one on one path, and one on another, as you did before, and have trouble. Stay together, and help one another."

"We will!" they answered, and really they meant to, but, you see, little pigs sometimes forget, just as real children do.

On they went together. Curly and his brother who hadn't any name, except that sometimes people called him "Bub," or maybe "Son," or even "Hey, Johnnie!" though that wasn't his real name at all.

Pretty soon, in about as long as it takes to eat a lollypop if you don't hurry to get down to the stick part of it - pretty soon the two piggie boys met Grandfather Squealer, who was the grandpapa of all the pigs in that part of the country,

"Oh, ho!" exclaimed the old gentleman pig, "Oh, ho! How are you today, Curly?"

"Very well, sir, thank you," replied the pig boy politely, and he looked around to see if the curly kink had come out of his tail where the bear had tied him to the round fence rail, but the curl was still there.

"And how is this other little chap?" went on Grandpa Squealer, as he took a pinch of snuff, and then looked in his vest pocket to see if he had any spare pennies. "How are you, Bub?" he asked. "You haven't any name yet, have you?"

"No sir," answered the brother of Curly. "I wish I had, though," and he also wished that Grandpa Squealer would find a penny so that he and his brother could buy a lollypop, and that wish came true, if you will kindly believe me. For the old gentleman pig did find two pennies.

"There now, boys," he said, "run along to the candy store. And maybe you can buy a name for yourself," and he playfully pulled the ears of Curly's brother. Then Grandpa Squealer sneezed again and walked on, and so did the two boy pigs.

"I'm going to buy a corn lollypop," said Curly.

"I think I'll buy a sour-milk one," said his brother, for you know little pigs, and big ones, too, like sour milk as much as you like yours sweet. Isn't that funny?

So they walked on together, talking of different things, and pretty soon they came to a place where there were two stores. One was painted red and the other was painted blue.

"I'm going in the red store for my lollypop," said Curly.

"Oh, let's go in the blue one," suggested his brother. "Maybe I can buy a name for myself in there. I am tired of being called 'Bub' and 'Johnny,' and names like that."

But the two brothers couldn't agree, so Curly went in the red store and his brother in the blue one. The blue store was kept by an old lady dog, and when the little pig, who, as yet, had no name, entered, the old lady dog storekeeper looked over the counter and asked:

"Well, little pig boy, what do you want?"

"If you please," he answered, "do you keep names to sell?"

"Why, what a funny question!" barked the dog lady. "The only names I have are names of candy, and I'm sure you don't want any of those, do you? There is peppermint and spearmint and cinnamon and lemon drops and cocoanut kisses and lollypops and jaw-breakers and tootsie rolls and chocolate - do you want any of those names?"

"No," replied the little pig boy, "I don't think I like any of those names for myself. I wouldn't want to be called Cocoanut Kisses, nor yet Lollypops, nor even Tootsie Rolls. Oh dear! I wish I could get a name such as my brother Curly has. But maybe I will some day. And now, if you please, I'll have a sour-milk lollypop."

So the old lady dog storekeeper gave it to the little pig boy, and he handed her his penny. He was just taking the paper off the lollypop, and was going to eat it - the lollypop, not the paper, you understand - and go out and see if his brother had come out of the red store, when, all of a sudden, a little puppy dog boy who had just come in from school saw the pig boy in the store, and right at him he sprang with a bow wow bark.

"Here! Come back!" cried the lady storekeeper who was the mother of the puppy dog boy. "Let that little pig alone."

"I'm only going to play tag with him," answered the puppy dog, and with that he sprang at the piggie and caught him by the ear. He really didn't mean to, but his teeth closed fast on poor piggie's ear, and there they stuck.

"Oh! Oh! Oh!" howled piggie. "I'm caught! Oh let me go. Please let me go!"

"Yes, let go of him at once, you naughty boy!" cried the doggie's mamma, as she made a grab for his tail. But just then piggie began to run, squealing as hard as he could, and as the doggie did not let go of his ear, the little barking chap was dragged along too. And then out from the red store ran Curly and he squealed and his brother squealed, also, and the boy dog barked, and so did the storekeeper lady dog, and such a time you never heard in all your life! Oh! such a racket!

"Let go my ear! Let go my ear!" squealed the pig, and the doggie boy tried to let go but he couldn't, until Curly got hold of him by the left leg and pulled him loose.

"Oh dear! Oh dear!" cried the piggie who had bought the sour milk lollypop. "Is my ear pulled off, Curly?"

"No, but it is hanging down like anything," said his brother. "I guess its broken!"

"Oh, I am so sorry!" exclaimed the little boy dog. "I didn't mean to do it. I was only going to tag you, but I slipped. Come in the house and my mamma will put some salve on your ear, and I'll give you an ice cream cone."

And just then Grandfather Squealer came past, and he saw Curly's little brother, with his ear hanging down, going flippity-flop, and the old gentleman said:

"Oh ho! I think I will call you Flopear, or Floppy for short. That is a good name, and it just fits you." And so after that the second little pig was always called Floppy for his ear never stood us again but always hung down like a bell clapper. But the salve soon made it well, and the storekeeper lady gave Floppy and Curly each an ice cream cone.

So that's all now, if you please, but in case the butcherman doesn't throw the loaf of bread at the candlestick and scare the lamp chimney I'll tell you in the story after this about Pinky Twistytail's rubber ball.

STORY III

PINKY'S RUBBER BALL.

"Now, children," exclaimed Mrs. Twistytail, the pig lady, one morning, when she had given Curly and Floppy and Baby Pinky their breakfast of sour milk with cornmeal stirred in it, "now, children, run out and play. I have the sweeping and dusting to do, and then I am going to make an apple pie."

"Oh, goodie!" cried Curly. "Do you want us to help you, mamma?"

"No, I'm afraid you would eat more apples than you would put in the pie," said Mrs. Twistytail with a laugh. "Run along now."

"Come on Curly," said Floppy and he ran out and turned a somersault, even though it was near winter, for he felt happy, now that he had a name and didn't have to be called "Bub" or "Johnny" or something like that.

"What shall we do?" asked Curly.

"Let's build a fort and play soldier," suggested Floppy. "Pinky can be a prisoner and we'll make believe capture her, and then we'll rescue her, and shoot off make-believe guns, and -"

"No - No!" cried Baby Pinky, as she tried to stand up on the end of her twisty tail, but she couldn't, for it was too slimpsy and not stiff enough. She fell down, but her brothers picked her up, and then the curl came back in her tail.

You see, after the bear had tied Curly to the fence and made his tail all frizzy-like, all the other pigs, including Pinky and Floppy wanted their tails to curl also, and their mamma had to do it for them, twisting them around the rolling-pin. And she even curled her own, and her husband's, that that's why all pigs have curly tails now, because it's stylish, you see.

"Why don't you want to play soldier?" asked Floppy of his little sister.

"Oh, it's too scary!" she said. "And the guns make so much noise. If you won't shoot off any guns I'll play."

"Pooh!" exclaimed Curly, "all soldiers have to shoot guns! You couldn't be a soldier with a gun that didn't make any noise."

"Then I'm not going to play," said Pinky, who was just the color of the inside of a shiny sea shell. "I'll bounce my rubber ball," she went on, "and you boys can play soldier."

So she bounced her ball that Grandfather Squealer had given her, while Curly and Floppy as I'll call him for short, made a fort out of cobs from which they had gnawed all the corn, and they had a fine time. They were off playing in the woods, while Pinky stayed near the house.

She was hoping her mamma would soon have the apple pie baked and would call her in and give her a piece, when, all of a sudden, as Pinky bounced her ball, it went high in the air, but it didn't come down again right away.

"My! What can have happened?" thought little Pinky, and she looked around, and there she saw a great big fuzzy fox, standing behind her. And the fox cried out, as he rubbed his nose:

"Did you hit me with that rubber ball?"

"Yes - yes - perhaps I did," said poor Baby Pinky, trembling so that she nearly shook the curl out of her tail. "I tossed my ball up in the air, but I'm sure I didn't mean to hit you with it. Please forgive me."

"No, indeed, I will not!" exclaimed the fox. "Your rubber ball hit me right on the nose when it came down, and I caught it. And, just for that, I am going to carry you away with me and make a pork pie of you!"

"Oh, please don't!" begged Pinky, shaking more than ever, and she squealed as loudly as she could, but her mamma did not hear her, for she was beating up some eggs to make a cake, and the egg beater made so much noise that she couldn't hear her own little girl. And Curly and Floppy were shooting off their make-believe guns, and making so much noise in the woods that they couldn't hear, and there was the fox about to carry off the poor little piggie girl to his den. Oh, wasn't it terrible?

"Here we go!" cried the fox, and with that he grabbed up poor Pinky, tossing her rubber ball on the ground. Up it bounced, and, hardly knowing what she did, the little pig girl caught it in her foot, holding it tight. Then the fox slung her across his back and ran off with her, Pinky squealing all the while as hard as she could.

"Squeal away!" growled the old fuzzy fox. "You'll soon stop it when I put you in the pork pie!"

And Pinky kept on squealing. Pretty soon the fox ran through the woods where Curly and Flop were playing soldier, but the fox didn't know that. Pinky did, however, and when she got beneath the trees she squealed louder than ever, hoping her brothers would hear.

"Keep quiet!" barked the fox.

"No! No!" exclaimed Pinky, and she squealed again. Oh! she squealed like anything. Then Curly heard her. So did Flop.

"That sounds like Pinky," said Curly, blinking his eyes.

"It surely does," agreed his brother. "Something must have happened to her." They ran out of the fort they had made of corncobs piled one on the other, and they saw their little baby sister being carried off by the fox. Wow! Think of that!

"Here, you let our Pinky alone!" cried Curly bravely.

"No! No! No!" answered the bad fox.

"Then we'll shoot you!" shouted Flop. "Shoot him, Curly!"

Then those two brave pig boys shot their make-believe guns at the fox. "Bang! Bang! Bung! Bung!" But do you s'pose he stopped for that? Not a bit of it! On he ran, faster than ever, carrying away Pinky, and Curly and Flop ran after him, but what could they do? It looked as if the little pig girl would soon be made into pork pie, when she suddenly called out:

"Oh, boys! My rubber ball! Fill it with water and squirt it at the fox!" and she threw her ball to Curly.

"Don't you dare squirt rubber-ball water at me!" howled the fox, for he was very much afraid of getting his tail wet.

"Yes we will!" shouted Curly and with that he caught the ball his sister tossed to him. It only took him a second to stop at a mud puddle and fill the ball with water. Then, taking careful aim, just as a brave pig soldier boy should, he squeezed the ball, and "Zip!" out squirted the water all over the bad fox.

"Oh wow! Double wow, and pumpkin pie! That water went right into my eye!" howled the fox, and then, with his tail all wet, so that it weighed ten pounds, or more, that fox was so utterly frightened and kerslostrated that he let go of poor little

Pinky and ran off to his den, and he didn't have any pork pie for a long time afterward.

"Oh, you saved me!" cried Pinky to her two brothers, when they had picked her up, and started back home with her.

"You helped save yourself," said Curly. "You and your rubber ball," and he and Flop were very glad their sister had not been carried off by the bad fox.

And on the next page, if the washtub doesn't fall out of its crib and knock a hole in the tea kettle so that all the lemonade runs out, I'll tell you how Curly helped his mamma.

STORY IV

HOW CURLY HELPED MOTHER

"Well, this is certainly a fine day for washing!" exclaimed Mrs. Twistytail, the pig lady, one morning as she got up from the nice, clean, straw bed where she had slept with little Pinky. "I must get right to work and hang out the sheets and pillow-cases so the sun will make them nice and white."

So she hurried through with the breakfast of sour milk with corn meal and sugar cakes, and as soon as Mr. Twistytail had gone to the factory, where he helped make sausage for buckwheat cakes, Mrs. Twistytail said:

"Now, children, do you want to help me wash?"

"Oh, yes, mamma!" they all cried at once.

"I'll turn the wringer," said Curly, "for I am good and strong."

"And I'll put the clothes pins in the basket and have them all ready," said Pinky, for, though she was only a little girl pig she could easily carry the clothes pins.

"What can I do?" asked Flop, the other little pig boy. His real name was Floppy, or Flop Ear, but I call him Flop for short you see.

"Oh, you can bring me in the sticks to make the fire," said his mamma, and soon the three piggie children were working away as fast as they could, helping their mamma, who was busy sorting out the clothes.

Soon the fire was made, and the sudsie-soapy water was boiling the clothes to sort of cook them nice and clean, and Pinky had the clothes pins all ready. Flop had put up the line, after he had brought in the firewood, and Curly was all ready with the wringer.

Well, you should have seen Mrs. Twistytail rub-adub-dub the clothes up and down on the washboard. My! how she did scatter the suds all over, and once some splashed right up in her eye, but she only laughed and sang a funny little song.

"Ready now, Curly!" she called to her eldest little boy. "Ready to wring out the clothes through the first water!"

So Curly turned the wringer, which doesn't ring like a bell, you know, but squeezes all the water out of the clothes so they will dry better. Around and around Curly turned the wringer handle, and the clothes came out like corn out of the poper.

"Oh, what fun!" cried the little pig boy, and his brother and sister thought it was very jolly to help their mamma.

"Now, you may run away and play for a while," said the pig lady. "I have to get the rinsing and bluing waters ready."

So Curly and Flop and Pinky ran out in the yard to play. Flop and Pinky saw a little boy and girl pig whom they knew, and they began playing, but Curly walked about, thinking maybe he might find a penny, when all of a sudden he saw his mamma hurrying out of the kitchen.

"Where are you going, mamma?" he called to her. "Is the washing all done? Can't I wring any more clothes?"

"Oh, yes," she answered. "There are plenty more to wring out even yet, but they must wait. Mrs. Littletail, who lives down the street, has just sent in to say that her little rabbit boy Sammie has the stomach ache and I am taking over some hot peppermint tea for him. The washing can wait until I get back."

On ran Mrs. Twistytail to make Sammie Littletail feel better, and just then her own little boy Curly had a great idea.

"I'll just slip in and finish the washing for mamma," he said to himself, as he saw that Flop and Pinky were still playing tag. "Won't she be s'prised when she comes in and sees the clothes all hung up to dry?"

So Curly hurried into the kitchen and there he saw a lot of water in a tub, and the pile of clothes in the basket ready to be rinsed and blued and hung out to dry. Then Curly began to help his mamma to make her surprised.

Into the tub he plumped the clothes, and then, fastening on the wringer, he began to wring them out as dry as he could. There were a lot of sheets and pillow-cases, and these last were like bags, full of wind and water when you put the open end in between the rubber rollers first. And then, when they came toward the closed end. My! how they would puff out and make a funny sissing noise.

Curly always liked to wring out the pillow-cases this way, and he had lots of fun. Soon he had a big basket of clothes ready to hang on the line. Wasn't he the smart little piggie boy, though?

Out into the yard he carried the basket of clothes. It was hard work, but he managed it. And how the wind did blow! It was all Curly could do to hold the big sheets from blowing away, but somehow he did, and he didn't want to call Flop or Pinky to help, for he wanted to surprise them, too, as well as his mamma.

Howard R. Garis

Well, he had hung up quite a lot of clothes to dry, and then came a large pillow-case. The wind was blowing harder than ever, and as Curly tried to hang the case on the line a big, strong breeze just took hold of it, puffed it out like a balloon, and then - and then, my goodness me, sakes alive! the wind took the pillow-case right up in the air, and as Curly was hanging tightly to it, he went up also!

Right up into the air he went, sailing and sailing, just like an aeroplane, and he cried out:

"Mamma! Papa! Flop Ear! Pinky! Save me!" But none of them heard him, and he went higher and higher until the pillow-case, full of air like a balloon, caught in a tree, and there was the little piggie boy held where he couldn't get down. Oh, dear me, wasn't that terrible?

Curly didn't know what to do. The tree was too big for him to jump down and he couldn't climb very well. He thought he would have to stay up there forever, maybe. But he didn't. Pretty soon Sammie Littletail's stomach ache was all better and Mrs. Twistytail came home. The first things she saw were the clothes hanging out on the line - that is, all but the pillow-case that had taken Curly up in the tall tree.

"My goodness me! sakes alive and a corn cob," exclaimed Mrs. Twistytail. "The children must have done this to help me. My, but I am surprised. But I wonder where they are?" Then she saw Flop and Pinky playing tag, but she couldn't see Curly.

"Oh, Curly, Curly, where are you?" she called, and her little boy answered:

"I'm up in the tree with the pillow-case!" Then his mamma saw him and she nearly fainted. But she didn't quite faint, and then she telephoned for a fireman with a long ladder, who came and got Curly safely down.

So that's how he helped his mamma, and he surprised her

more than he meant to, but it all came out right in the end. And soon the washing was all done, and the firemen gave each of the pig children a penny.

So that's all now, but in the next story, in case the oil can doesn't slide down the clothes pole and break the handle off the pump, so the angle worm can't get his ice cream cone, I'll tell you about Curly and the elephant.

STORY V

CURLY AND THE ELEPHANT

When Curly Twistytail, the little pig boy, was digging away with his nose in the front yard, one day, hunting for lollypops, or maybe ice cream cones, under the grass, for all that I know; one day, I say, as he was rooting away, he heard his mamma calling:

"Oh, Curly; Oh, Flop Ear! I want some one to go to the store for me."

"That means I've got to go," thought Curly, as he looked around to see if his tail was still kinked into a little twist.

"I'll have to go because Flop is off playing ball with Bully the frog. Well, there's no use getting cross about it," so, giving a cheerful grunt or two, just to show that he didn't at all mind, Curly ran around to the back door and said:

"What is it, mamma? I'll go to the store for you?"

"Oh, there you are!" exclaimed Mrs. Twistytail. "Well, I want a dozen eggs, and be sure to get fresh ones, and don't smash them on the way home."

"I won't," said the little piggie boy, and with that he ran down the street squealing a tune about a little monkey who hung down by his tail, and when he went to sleep he sat inside the water pail.

Well, Curly got the eggs all right, and he was on his way home with them, when, all at once, as he came to the corner of the woods, where an old stump stood, out from behind it jumped a bad dog.

"Ha, what have you in that bag, little piggie boy?" asked the bad dog, catching hold of Curly by his ear so that he could not run away.

"Eggs," answered Curly. "There are eggs in this bag for a cake my mamma is going to bake."

"No, you are mistaken," said the dog, gritting his teeth. "Those eggs are for me, I want to eat them," and he reached out his paw for the paper bag.

Now, though Curly did not know it, this was a bad egg dog - that is, he liked to eat eggs raw, without ever boiling or frying them, and that kind of a dog is the worst there is. No one likes him, not even the old rooster who crows in the morning.

"I'll just take those eggs," said the bad dog, and, though I don't know how to make a cake, still I can manage to eat them," and with that he took an egg out of the bag, chipped a little hole in the shell, and drank up the yellow and white part just as you would drink an ice cream soda. And, mind you, that dog never even winked an eye! What do you think of that?

"Number one!" the dog exclaimed, as he reached for another egg. "Now for number two!"

And oh! how badly Curly felt when he saw his mamma's eggs going that way. It was almost as bad as if he had dropped the bag on the sidewalk and smashed them, only, of course, it was not his fault.

Then the little piggie boy decided to be brave and bold. The

Howard R. Garis

bad dog was eating the second egg, and he had his nose tipped up in the air, so the white and yellow of the egg would run out of the shell down his throat, when, all of a sudden, Curly pulled himself loose from the dog's paw and grabbed up the bag with the ten eggs in it and ran away as fast as he could.

"Here! Come back!" cried the bad egg dog, as he threw the empty shell at Curly. "Come back here with the rest of my eggs!"

"Your eggs! No indeed!" cried Curly, and he didn't in the least mind when the egg shell hit him on the end of his nose, for, being empty, you understand, the shell didn't hurt any more than a piece of paper would have done.

"Ha! If you won't come back I'll chase after you!" barked the bad egg dog, and with that he began chasing after Curly.

Faster and faster ran Curly, and faster and faster came the dog after him, until he had nearly caught the little piggie boy. Then Curly thought to himself:

"Well, maybe if I roll one more egg to him he'll stop to eat that and let me alone. Anyhow, nine eggs will be enough for a cake, and I can tell mamma how it happened that the others were lost."

So the piggie boy stopped running long enough to take an egg out of the bag and roll it along the sidewalk toward the dog.

"Ah, ha!" growled the dog. "Egg Number Three!" and he stopped to eat the yellow and white part of it. Of course, Curly ran on, and he got some distance ahead, but you see the more eggs the dog ate the faster he could run, so on he came, and he had almost caught up to Curly when the little piggie boy thought again:

"Well, here goes for another egg!"

So he rolled a second one toward that bad dog, who ate it, hardly stopping at all, and on he came again.

"Now, I have you!" the dog cried, as he threw the empty shell at Curly, striking him on the nose once more. "Now, I'll get all the eggs, and besides, I'll bite your tail off for running away!"

"Oh, how dreadful!" thought Curly, and he wondered how it would feel to have no tail. He was running as fast as he could, and he was wishing a policeman or fireman would save him from the bad dog, when, all at once, out from a yard with a high fence around it sprang something big and white, with yellow legs, and there came a hissing sound, just as if water were being squirted out of a hose. Then a voice said:

"Here, you bad dog, let my friend Curly alone! Run away, now, or I'll nip you on your toes and nose! Skip! Hiss! Scoot!"

And that dog was so frightened that he didn't think a single thing more about eggs, but he just tucked his tail between his legs, where it wouldn't get in his way, and off he ran.

"Oh, saved at last!" gasped Curly, as he sat down on the curbstone to rest, "and I still have eight eggs left for mamma's cake." Then he looked up to see who had rescued him, and it was old Grandfather Goosey Gander, the father of all the geese. The brave creature had hissed at the bad egg dog and frightened him away.

"Oh, how thankful I am to you," said Curly, politely, "and when the cake is baked you shall have a piece, Grandpa Goosey."

So he went on home with the rest of the eggs and - well, I do declare! I have forgotten all about the elephant! I know he was to be in this story, somewhere, but there's no room now, so I'll have to put him in the next one, which will be about Flop and the bag of meal - that is, if the clothes-basket doesn't fall on the gas stove and make the rice pudding go down the cellar to hide away from the rag doll.

STORY VI

FLOP AND THE BAG OF MEAL

Now, let me see, I promised to put in this story, something about the elephant; didn't I? That's because I left it out of the story on the page before this, where Curly had such a dreadful time with the bad egg dog.

Well, now, if I leave the elephant out of this story I promise that I'll give each one of you an ice cream cone with a raisin in it. All you'll have to do - in case I forget to tell about the elephant and how he helped Flop - all you have to do, I say, is to come up to my house and say "Magoozilum!" at me, just like that, and turn two somersaults on the parlor rug, and the ice cream cone is yours for the asking.

But now let's get right at the story. You see it happened this way. Once upon a time, when Curly and his brother Flop were out in the yard of the piggy-house, playing "ring around the apple tree," their mother called to them:

"Oh, boys! come in here!" she said, and when they got to the kitchen where she was working, she asked them: "Do you know what I'm making?"

"Pies," said Curly.

"Pudding," suggested Flop, as he tried to make his slimpsy ear stand up straight, but he couldn't.

"Neither one," said their mother. "But if one of you will go to the store for me I'll make a Johnny cake for supper."

"A Johnny cake?" asked Curly. "Is it called that because a boy has to be named Johnny to eat it?"

"No," answered his mother with a laugh, "but lots of boys named Johnny do eat it. However, just at the last minute I find that I have no corn meal. Now who wants to go to the store for a bag full, so I can make the Johnny cake?"

"I went for the eggs, last time," said Curly, sort of slow and thoughtful like.

"Then I suppose it's Flop's turn to go for the bag of meal," said his mother. "But I do hope the bad dog doesn't chase him."

"Oh, I'm not afraid, mamma," said the little piggie boy. "If he comes after me I'll throw corn meal dust in his nose and make him sneeze, and then he can't see to catch me."

"Very well," said Mrs. Twistytail, so she gave Flop the money for the bag of meal. Off he started to the store, while his brother, Curly, went back in the yard to play hop-skip-and-jump, all by himself.

Flop went along the street, whirling his tail in a little circle like a pin-wheel, or a merry-go-round, and he was thinking how good the Johnny cake would taste, when, all of a sudden, he heard a noise.

It was a noise something like thunder, yet not quite so loud, and Flop was wondering what it was, when, all at once, as he turned around the corner, he saw a big elephant sitting on a stump, and crying as hard as he could cry. And this elephant had made the noise.

Ah ha! That's the time I caught you; I've got the elephant in this story after all, so you can't have the ice cream cones this time. But never mind, maybe some other day you may.

Anyhow, there was the elephant crying, and he shed as many tears as you could cry in a year, even if you've been vaccinated. And Flop instead of being afraid, went right up to the big creature and said, most politely:

"What is the matter? Can I help you?"

"Eh? What's that?" exclaimed the elephant. "Bless my trunk strap! It's a little pig. Oh dear!"

"What is the matter?" asked Flop.

"Oh, I ran a big sliver in my left hind foot," said the elephant, "and I can't get it out. I've tried to pull it with my tail, but my tail isn't long enough, and I can't even reach it with my trunk. And I was to go to the codfish ball tonight, and now I can't, for I never could dance with a sliver in my foot."

"Perhaps I can pull it out," said Flop, and when the elephant held up his foot, which was nearly as large as a washtub, the little piggie boy could see the splinter as plainly as anything.

"I'll get it out," he exclaimed and then he wound his kinky, curly tail around the splinter and pulled it right out of the elephant's foot as quick as a wink.

"Oh, how kind of you!" cried the big creature. "If ever I can do you a favor I will. Now I can go to the party tonight and dance. But I'll just sit here awhile and rest, before I go."

So Flop went on to the store to get the corn meal, and he told the man about how Mrs. Twistytail was going to make a Johnny cake and how he had pulled the splinter out of the elephant's foot, and the store man said:

"You are a brave little piggie boy, and here is a lollypop

Howard R. Garis

for you."

Well, Flop was on his way home, carrying the bag of meal, and he was taking little nips and nibbles off the lolly-pop, when all at once what should happen but that, out from behind a tree sprang the bad skillery-scalery alligator.

"Ah, ha!" he cried. "Now I have you. Now for some roast pork and apple sauce!" and he made a grab for Flop, but he didn't quite catch him, I'm glad to say. And how that little piggie boy did run! Faster and faster he ran, carrying the bag of meal for the Johnny cake, but still the 'gator came after him and almost had him.

"Oh, will no one save me?" cried Flop, for he could hardly run any more, and then all of a sudden, he came to the place where the elephant was still sitting on a stump, resting himself.

"Oh, help me! Help me!" cried Flop.

"Indeed, I will!" shouted the elephant. And with that, in his strong trunk, he lifted Flop up on his broad back. Still the skillery-scalery alligator came on, and he cried in his rasping voice:

"I want that pig!"

"Oh you do, eh?" asked the elephant, sarcastic like. "Well, you can't have him. Take that!" and then the elephant just reached around back with his trunk and took some corn meal out of the bag that Flop held and the elephant blew the meal in the alligator's eyes and nose and mouth and then -

"A-choo! Aker-choo! Boo-hoo! Hoo hoo! Splitzie-doo! Foo-foo!" sneezed the alligator, turning forty-'leven somersaults. "Oh, dear me, what a cold I have!" and he sneezed so hard that all of his back teeth dropped out, and he couldn't bite any one for nearly a week. And then he crawled off, leaving Flop to go home in peace and quietness and watch his mamma make a

Johnny cake.

And when the cake was baked they gave the kind elephant some to take to the codfish ball with him, and that's the end of this story, if you please.

But on the next page, if I have left any of those ice cream cones with raisins inside, to give to the trolley car conductor when he punches my transfer, I'll tell you about the piggie boys at school.

STORY VII

PIGGY BOYS AT SCHOOL

One day Curly, the little pig who had such a funny shaped tail, said to his brother, Flop Ear:

"Say, let's run off and look for adventures as Uncle Wiggily, the old gentleman rabbit, used to do!"

"Where shall we run?" asked Flop.

"Oh, almost anywhere," answered Curly. "We'll go down the road, toward Sylvan Way, and out beyond the old black stump, and turn the corner around the place where the apple tree grows, and then we'll see what will happen."

"All right," agreed Flop, so the two little pig brothers started off. Their mamma was making some red flannel pies in the kitchen, ready for winter, and of course she did not see them go, or perhaps she might have stopped them.

Pretty soon, in a little while, oh, maybe in about an hour and a half, Curly and Flop came to a building all made of red brick, with a chimney sticking from the top for the smoke to come out of, and a lot of doors and windows in it.

"I wonder what that is?" said Flop.

"Maybe it's where the skillery scalery alligator lives,"

suggested Curly.

"Oh, no, he lives in a rocky cave under the water," spoke Flop. "This isn't his house."

"Then it's where the bad fox lives," went on Curly as he put his nose down in the dirt to see if he could find any hickory nuts there.

"No, the fox lives in a stump," said Flop. "I don't know what this place can be."

And then, all of a sudden, before you could take a brush and paint a picture of a lion on a soda cracker, all of a sudden the piggie boys heard a lot of voices singing a song like this:

"We are little children,
To school we love to go;
We run along,
And sing a song,
In rain or hail or snow."

"Oh, ho!" exclaimed Curly. "That's a school, that's what it is."

"To be sure," agreed his brother. "Let's go in and learn our A B C's and then we can go home and tell mamma all about it. This is an adventure, all right."

"I believe it is," said Curly. So the two little piggy boys walked along through the front door of the school, right into the room where the nice lady bug teacher was telling the children how to make a straight line crooked by bending it, and how to put butter on their bread, by spreading it.

"Oh, my!" exclaimed a little rabbit girl, as she saw the two piggie boys in school. "Look at that!"

"Quiet! No talking!" said the lady bug teacher.

"Oh, but this is like Mary's little lamb, only it's different," said Jonny Bushytail, the squirrel boy, as he remembered the verse about the lamb in school. Only this time it was pigs.

And, all this while Curly and Flop just stood there, in the school room looking about them and wondering what they had better do. For they had never been to school before; not even in the kindergarten class.

"This is a funny place," said Flop.

"Isn't it?" agreed Curly. "They all seem quite surprised to see us."

"They do, indeed," agreed Flop and, as a matter of fact, all the animal children in the school were laughing. But the teacher – she didn't laugh. Instead, she said:

"Quiet, if you please! Fold your paws, everybody! Now, that the little pigs have come to school we must see how much they know, so we can tell what class to put them in." So she said to Curly:

"Spell cat:"

"D-o-g," spelled the little pig boy.

"Wrong," said the teacher. "I guess you will have to go in the kindergarten class." Then she said to Flop Ear; "Spell boy."

"G-i-r-l," spelled Flop.

"Wrong," said the teacher. "You, too, will have to go in the kindergarten class. Now, I wonder if either of you piggy boys can make a paper bird in a cage."

So she gave each of them a pair of scissors and some red paper, and blue and pink and yellow and brown and all colors like that. But my goodness sakes alive and some candy with cocoanut on the top! Curly and Flop had never learned to cut things out of paper, and of course they did not know how. They just cut and slashed and didn't make anything but scrips and scraps.

"Oh, dear!" exclaimed the teacher. "Such piggie boys I never saw! They can't even be in the baby kindergarten class!"

"Maybe they can do something," said Susie Littletail's new baby sister. "Some trick or anything like that."

"Of course we can!" cried Curly, who was ashamed that his brother and himself could do nothing the teacher asked. "Just watch us!" he cried.

So he stood up on the end of his tail and spun around like a top, and then he made a squealing noise like a horn and played a tune called "Ham and Eggs are Very Fine, but Ice Cream Cones are Better." Then Flop turned a somersault and stood on one leg, and then the two piggie boys danced up and down together like leaves falling off a tree.

"Oh! those little fellows are smarter than I thought they were," said the lady bug teacher. "I guess they can be in our first class after all."

And just then a great big, bad, black bear rushed into the schoolroom, and he was going to grab up about forty-'leven of the animal children.

But Curly suddenly shouted:

"Here, you scoot away from us or I'll make a bee sting you on the nose!" and as the bear was very much afraid of being stung on the end of his soft and tender nose, he ran away as fast as he could and stayed in his den, eating postage stamps for nearly a week, and didn't bother anybody.

Then the teacher and all the animal children thought the

piggie boys were very clever indeed, and the lady bug invited them to come to school whenever they wanted to. And Curly and Flop said they would come.

Then they ran home to dinner and that's all there is to this story. But on the next page, in case the little girl with brown eyes doesn't cut all the green grass for the rag baby's hair ribbon, I'll tell you about Curly being vaccinated.

STORY VIII

CURLY IS VACCINATED

About two days, or maybe three days and part of another one, after Curly Twistytail and his brother, Flop, had run away to school and had performed their funny tricks, as I told you in the story before this one, something else happened. And this is the way it was:

Curly was out in the yard in front of the piggy house one morning, raking up the leaves and thinking what fun he would have making a fire and roasting some ears of corn, when he heard his mamma calling:

"Oh, boys! Where are you?"

"Here I am," answered Curly as he jumped over a pile of leaves and fell into the middle of them. But it did not hurt him, as they were so nice and soft.

"And here I am, too!" exclaimed Flop, and the other little piggie boy, who was up in a hammock, swinging with one of the Katy Dids, jumped down and ran to the back kitchen door.

"What is it, mother?" called both the little piggie boys together.

"I want one of you to go to the store for me," she said, "I need some chocolate to put on top of a cake."

"Oh, I'll go!" exclaimed Floppy and Curly together, quickly, and you could not tell which one spoke first. But Mrs. Twistytail said:

"Well, I think I'll let Floppy go, and when he comes back I'll give you each some of the cake."

So off Flop ran to the store, squealing as hard as anything because he was so happy. At first Curly felt a little sad that he couldn't go to the store, for the man who kept it always gave the piggie boys a sweet cracker or something like that. But, of course, only one was needed to carry the chocolate.

"Never mind," said Curly's mamma to him. "You may go next time."

So then he felt better, and he was thinking what fun it would be to have a piece of chocolate cake, when all of a sudden he stopped to think.

"I guess I'll go to school again!" he exclaimed. "That will be fun. Yes, I'll go to school!"

So off he started, while his brother was getting the chocolate at the store, and pretty soon Curly came to the place where the lady bug school teacher had her classes of animal children in a hollow stump.

Curly knocked at the door, and when the teacher came to open it he made his best bow.

"Well, what is it, little piggie boy?" asked the teacher, kindly.

"If you please," said Curly, "I want to come to school."

"Very good," said the teacher. "I think you may. You and your brother were so kind as to scare off the bear, so you may come to our class. But, first, let me ask you - have you been vaccinated?"

"Vaccinated?" repeated Curly. "Is that like a lollypop?"

"No, that is having the doctor scratch your leg with a toothpick so you won't get sick and have the epizootic," said the teacher. "Let me see your paw."

So she looked at Curly's paw, which he held out, and she saw that he had never been vaccinated, so she said he would have to have that done to him before he could come to school every day.

"You go home," said the teacher to the little piggie boy, "and get vaccinated. Then come back in about a week."

So, as Curly wanted to go to school very much, on his way home he went past Dr. Possum's office. And going in, he said:

"I want to be vaccinated, doctor, so I can go to school."

"Very well," answered Dr. Possum. "We'll do it."

So Curly rolled up his sleeve, and the doctor scratched his paw with a toothpick, and put some funny kind of yellow salve on it, and wrapped it up in a little celluloid cap to keep the snowflakes from it, and also that no mosquitos could bite it.

"Now, in about a week your arm will begin to itch," said the doctor, "and it will tickle you, and then, after a bit, you will be vaccinated, and you can go to school."

"Very good," said Curly, and he wondered why all little animal children had to be vaccinated, and have the mumps and the measles-pox and epizootic, and all things like that, but he couldn't guess, and so he didn't try.

He was rolling down his sleeve, and Dr. Possum was putting

away the toothpick with which he had vaccinated the little piggie boy, when, all of a sudden, into the room jumped a big fuzzy fox, crying out:

"Oh, Joy! Oh, good luck! Oh, hungriness! Here I have a pig dinner and an opossum dinner all at once! Oh, happiness!"

Then he made a jump, and was just going to grab Dr. Possum and Curly too, when the little piggie boy cried out:

"Vaccinate him! Vaccinate him, Dr. Possum. That will make him so itchy that he can't bite us,"

"The very thing!" cried Dr. Possum, and before the big fuzzy fox could get out of the way Dr. Possum vaccinated him on the end of his nose with the toothpick all covered with the funny yellow salve, and the fox was so kerslostrated that he jumped over his tail seven times, and then leaped out of the window, leaving Curly and Dr. Possum in peace. And in about a week - oh, how that fox's nose did itch! Wow! And some sandpaper besides!

As for Curly, he was vaccinated very nicely, indeed, and he could go to school when his arm got well. And what happened next I'll tell you in the story after this, and it will be about Curly and the spinning top - that is, it will if the pink parasol coming up the street doesn't slip on the horse chestnut and make the pony cart fall down the coal hole.

STORY IX

CURLY AND THE SPINNING TOP

"Oh dear!" cried Curly one morning, before his papa, Mr. Twistytail, the pig gentleman, had started for work. "Oh dear, how dreadful I feel!"

"Why, what is the matter?" asked his papa, as he looked in the back of the shiny dishpan to see if his collar was on straight.

"Oh, my arm hurts so!" went on Curly. "It all seems swelled up, and it has a lump under it and I don't feel a bit good. Oh dear!"

"It's his vaccination," said his mamma. "It is beginning to 'take' now, and it pains him."

"What is beginning to 'take', mamma?" asked Curly. "It is beginning to take the pain away? Because if it isn't I wish it was. Oh dear!"

"It will soon be better," said Mrs. Twistytail. "Would you like some nice yellow cornmeal ice cream, or some lollypops, flavored with sour milk?"

"Neither, mamma," answered the piggie boy. "But I would like something to amuse me."

"All right," answered the pig lady. "Then I'll send Flop Ear

Howard R. Garis

down to the store to get you a toy. Come Floppy," she called, "go and get something with which to amuse your brother," for you see Flop hadn't yet been vaccinated, and his arm was not sore.

"What would you like?" asked Flop of his brother. "Shall I get you a mouth organ, or a kite, so you can fly away up to the clouds?"

"Neither one," said Curly. "I want a spinning top that I can make go around when I lie down in bed. And I want it to make music and jump around on a plate and slide on a string and all things like that."

"All right," said Flop Ear. "I'll try to get it for you."

So he went down to the eleven-and-six-cent store to buy a spinning top for his brother. And he found it, too. It was a top all painted red and blue and yellow and green, and when you wound it up, and pressed a spring, it spun around and around as fast as anything, making soft and low music like the wind blowing through the trees on a summer night, and sending the mosquitoes all sailing away to the north pole.

"I know Curly Tail will like this," said Flop Ear.

So the store man wrapped the top up for him in a nice piece of blue paper, tied with a pink string, just the kind they have in the drug store, and Flop started back with the top to amuse his little sick, vaccinated brother.

And when Curly saw that top, all colored red and green, and blue and yellow and skilligminkpurple, as it was, he felt better at once, and, sitting up in bed, he began to spin it on a nice smooth board that his brother brought up from the woodpile for him.

Around and around on the board spun the top, looking like a pinwheel on the night before Fourth of July, and Curly's sore arm began to feel better all at once.

Then Flop started to run down in the yard to play hop scotch with Peetie and Jackie Bow Wow, the puppy dogs, and Curly said:

"Some day, Flop, when you've been vaccinated, I'll get you a top to amuse you."

"Thank you," spoke Flop most politely, as he slid down the banisters and bumped off on the last step with a bounce.

So Curly played with his spinning top, and his brother was down in the yard, having fun, when, all at once in at the window where Curly was in bed, jumped a great big snail. Now a snail is an animal that has horns, and he lives in a shell that grows on his back, and he goes very slowly. But sometimes, when he has eaten red pepper for his lunch, he can go as fast as anything. And this was what had happened to this snail. He had eaten red pepper, and he fairly jumped in at the window where Curly was lying in bed.

"Bur-r-r-r!" warbled the snail, "Here I am," and he made a grab for the little piggie boy, for he was a very large snail indeed, as big as a dog house.

"Look out for my vaccination!" cried Curly. "Don't hit my arm, please."

"Oh, what do I care for vaccinations!" cried the snail. "If you don't give it to me at once, so I can throw it away, I'll stick you with my horns," and he wiggled them at Curly just as a mooley cow would have done.

"Give you my vaccination!" cried Curly. "Why, how can I, when it's fast on my leg?"

"No matter!" snapped and snipped the snail. "Give it to me at once," and he reached over, and he was just going to squeeze

Curly Tail's vaccination, and maybe hurt him like anything for all I know, when, all of a sudden, the little piggie boy thought of his spinning top.

It was all wound up, ready to spin, so Curly just pushed the spring, and whizzicum-whazzicum, around and around went the top, on the board in bed, right in front of the snail. And when the queer creature, with his home on his back, saw it he cried out:

"Oh, merry-go-rounds! Oh, pin wheels! Oh, circus hoops!" For it made him dizzy to see the top spinning around, you see. "Stop it!" he begged, but Curly would not, and at last the snail got so dizzy from watching the spinning top that he fell right over backward on it, and around and around he went, faster and faster, until, all of a sudden, just as when you get off a merry-go-round before it stops moving, that snail was tossed off from the top right out of the window into the mulberry bush, where he belonged, and so he didn't stick Curly with his horns after all. Wasn't that good?

So that's how Curly, with his spinning top, got the best of the snippery snail, and a few days later the little piggy boy could go to school whenever he wanted, for his vaccination was all better. And as for that snail, well, the less said about him the better - at least in this story.

And pretty soon, in case the man who is taking up the dried leaves in the street, doesn't put the rag baby in his bag and take her off to gather chestnuts, I'll tell you about Flop Ear and the frozen turtle.

STORY X

FLOP AND THE TURTLE

"Bur-r-r! Whew! Ice cream!" exclaimed Curly, the little piggie boy, one morning, as he hopped out of his bed in the clean straw and ran to the head of the stairs to see if breakfast was ready. "It's cold! Terrible cold!"

"Of course it is," agreed Flop, his brother. "It will soon be winter and time for chestnuts and popcorn and sliding down hill and all that. Of course it's cold."

"I hope there is some warm water to wash in," went on Curly.

"Warm water! What's that!" cried his papa from the next room. "Nonsensicalness! Cold water is better for you. It will make your skin nice and rosy. Wash in cold water."

So Curly, whether he wanted to or no, had to sozzle and splash himself all over in cold water, and really it did him good, for it made him feel nice and warm and made his ears and nose as red as a pink flannel blanket.

Then the two piggie boys were ready for breakfast, and they had hot corn meal cakes, with sour-milk and maple syrup sprinkled on them, and eggs, with the shells taken off, and warm milk and all things like that.

Then it was time for Curly to go to school, but as for Flop, he had not yet been vaccinated, and so he could not go to blackboard classes and learn how to add two and two together and make a mud pie of them, or how to write his name with red chalk that made blue marks.

"What are you going to do while I'm at school?" asked Curly of his little piggie brother, who was playing in the front yard.

"Oh, I think I'll build myself a little house out of corncobs," said Flop, "and then I'll go over and tell Jennie Chipmunk that she can put her rag doll to sleep in it."

"Fine!" cried Curly. "And when I come home from school I'll bring you each a lollypop."

So Curly put on his warm checker-pattern coat and stuck his paws in little red mittens, for it was quite cold that morning, and off he went to school.

But his brother, who had to stay home because he was not vaccinated, looked out in the yard, and pretty soon he said:

"Oh, I guess I'll go out and take a walk. Maybe I can find something or have an adventure."

So out Flop walked in the yard, and pretty soon, in a little while, not so very long, he came to a place where there was something that looked like a black stone with yellow marks on it.

"That's just what I'm looking for," said Flop, as he saw the queer stone. "I heard my mamma saying the other day that she needed some weight to keep the kitchen door from blowing shut. This stone will be the very thing for her."

So over he ran to where he saw the thing that looked like a stone, and he picked it up, no matter if it was cold. For there was frost on the ground - white frost that made everything look as though a little shower of snow had fallen - and everything was cold and frozen.

Into the house ran Flop, the little piggie boy, carrying his black stone, all streaked with yellow.

"Oh, see what I have found for you, mamma!" he exclaimed. "It will keep the kitchen door from blowing shut."

"So it will," said his mamma. "What a kind boy you are." So she took the stone and placed it where it would keep the kitchen door from slamming, and going shut, and then she made a custard pie so that Curly could have some when he came home from school.

Pretty soon the pie was done, and Flop was almost asleep in the nice warm kitchen waiting for his piece. His mamma suddenly called to him:

"Flop, will you watch the pie for a minute while I run across the street and borrow a yeast cake from Mrs. Wibblewobble, the duck lady?"

"Yes, of course I will," said Flop, rubbing his sleepy eyes. Then he looked all around the kitchen, and on the table where it was cooling he saw the nice pies his mamma had made, and he thought how good a piece would be, and then he also saw something else.

Into the kitchen came creeping a bad old egg dog - the same one who had tried to get the eggs from Curly a few days before.

"Pies!" cried the bad egg dog! "Custard pies! How I love 'em! Yum-yum!" and with that he made a jump and he was just going to eat the lovely custard pie Mrs. Twistytail had made when Flop said:

"Here, you let that pie alone, if you please. It isn't yours. It's my mamma's."

"No matter!" growled the bad egg dog. "I will eat it anyhow, and you can't stop me!"

And with that he started to throw Flop out of the window, but the little piggie boy cried:

"Oh, what shall I do? Will no one help me?"

"Yes, of course. I will!" answered a voice, and then that queer object, which Flop had thought was a stone, began to move. Out of a shell came a long neck, and a head with a sharp mouth on the end, and out came four sharp claws, and instead of a stone there was a mud turtle as large as life. Really there was, I'm not fooling a bit!

"I'll help you!" cried the brave turtle.

"Oh, you!" said Flop. "I thought you were a stone to keep the kitchen door from swinging shut."

"No, I am a turtle - a frozen turtle," said the voice. "At least I WAS frozen. The cold weather made me so slimpsy-slopsy that I couldn't move, if you will kindly excuse me saying so. But as soon as I got warmed up in your nice kitchen I became as lively as ever. I'll soon fix that dog. Watch me!"

And all of a sudden the turtle bit that dog on the end of its tail, and the dog ran off howling, and so he didn't get any of the nice pie, and he didn't bother Flop, nor Curly and his vaccination, any more, and that night they gave the turtle some hot lemonade so he wouldn't catch any more cold from having been almost frozen by the frosts. And as for that dog, why a dentist pulled one of his ears next day.

So you see what Flop thought was a stone turned out to be a frozen turtle who did him a great favor. And ever after that whenever Mrs. Twistytail made pie the turtle was always in the kitchen to keep the door open, and drive out any bad dogs in case they happened to get in.

And so no more now, if you please, as I am sleepy, and I know you must be, too. But in case the little girl in Montclair doesn't drop her doll on the sidewalk, and spill the sawdust all over the stick of molasses candy I'll tell you next about Curly and the chestnuts.

STORY XI

CURLY AND THE CHESTNUTS

"Why, Curly," exclaimed the nice old lady owl school teacher one day, when the class in drawing was doing its lesson. "Why, Curly Twistytail! I'm certainly surprised at you!"

Of course, all the animal children looked over at the little piggie boy, and at his brother Flop, also; but Flop had done nothing. And what do you suppose it was that Curly had done?

Why, instead of drawing a picture of a pail of sour milk, as the teacher had told him to do, he had made a picture of a monkey-doodle sitting on top of a Jack o'Lantern pumpkin. Wasn't that just awful! Well, I guess yes, and some tooth brushes besides.

"Oh, Curly, how could you?" asked the owl teacher, in a sorrowful voice.

"I - I didn't mean to," spoke the little piggie boy. "I - I guess it just - happened."

You see, during the drawing lesson, when the animal children were supposed to make different pictures on their papers, the teacher would fly around the room softly and come up from behind the desks. Thus, she could look over the animal children's shoulders and see what they were doing, when they didn't know it. It was then that she had seen what Curly, the pig, drew.

"Well, Curly," went on the owl teacher, sadly, "of course, it was wrong of you to make that kind of a picture, and, though I do not like to do it, I shall have to punish you. You will have to stay in after school."

And so that's how it was that Curly did not go out with the other animal children when school was dismissed. He had to stay in and clean off the blackboards, but he didn't mind that much, and really he was sorry for being a little bit bad.

"You may go now," said the owl school teacher, after a while, and Curly hurried home, feeling a little sad, and wondering what his mamma would say to him. He also wanted to hurry and have some fun with his brother, Flop.

Well, as Curly was going through the woods, all of a sudden, under a tree, something fell and hit him on the nose. He jumped to one side and exclaimed:

"Who is throwing stones at me?"

But no one answered, and Curly went on. Soon something else fell down, and hit him on the ear.

"I say!" he cried. "Would you please stop that? Is that the skillery-scalery alligator, or the fuzzy fox?"

But no one answered him, and Curly hurried on, thinking that perhaps bad fairies might be trying to have fun with him, or maybe turn him into a ham, or a piece of bacon, or something like that.

Well, he had not gone on much farther when, all at once, another something pattered down from a high tree, and struck him on the nose again.

"Oh, I say!" cried Curly, "please stop!" for this time it had been something sharp that hit him. "That isn't fair!" went on the little piggie boy. "Who is throwing things at me?"

He looked down on the ground, and there he saw something like a rubber ball, only it was a sort of greenish brown color, and had stickers all over on it. And then it burst open, and out rolled three little brown things.

"My word!" cried Curly, just like an English piggie boy. "My word! What is this?"

"Ha! Ha!" laughed a voice behind him, and turning quickly around Curly saw Jacko Kinkytail, a hand organ monkey, hanging by his tail from a tree branch. "Ha! Ha!" laughed the monkey again. "Don't you know what those brown things on the ground are?"

"No indeed," replied the piggie boy. "What are they?"

"Chestnuts," said Jacko the hand organ monkey. "They are chestnuts, and they fell off the trees and hit you. No one was throwing stones at you, though the prickly burrs inside of which the chestnuts are, seem as large as stones."

"Chestnuts, eh?" spoke Curly. "What good are they?"

"To eat," answered the monkey. "We will build a fire and roast some, and you will like them very much."

"Goodie-oodie!" squealed Curly, and, as he and the monkey began to gather up the chestnuts, the piggie boy was rather glad, after all, that he had been kept in, though of course he was sorry that he had made the wrong picture in drawing class.

So while Curly gathered up the chestnuts, rooting them out from under the leaves with his nose, that was like a piece of rubber, and stamping them out of the prickly burrs with his sharp feet - while he was doing this, I say, the monkey was making a fire to roast the nuts.

Soon Curly had quite a pile of them by an old stump, and the monkey had built a hot fire.

"Now, we will roast the chestnuts," spoke Jacko, and he put several pawsful on the hot coals.

"And when will they be roasted?" asked Curly.

"Soon," answered the monkey. "We will have a game of tag while we are waiting."

And, all of a sudden, as they were playing tag, out from under a big flat stone, came the bad skillery-scalery alligator, with a tin horn on his back. Oh! but he was a bad fellow!

"Ah, ha!" he cried. "Now I have you! Now I will have a piggie boy to eat and a monkey boy to wait on the table. Come along, both of you!" and the bad alligator made a grab for the two friends and was about to carry them off to his den.

"Oh, please let me go!" begged Curly.

"Yes do!" asked the monkey. "Let us go."

"No! No!" snapped the alligator. And just then there sounded this noise:

"Bang! Bang! Snap! Crack! Bang! Boom!"

"Oh I what is that?" cried the 'gator. "Oh! the hunters with their guns are after me. I must run! This is no place for me!"

Then, dropping Curly and the monkey, the bad alligator ran away as fast as he could, and didn't hurt either of them, and the "bang-bang!" noises kept getting louder and louder.

"Oh, what are they?" asked Curly, who was almost as much

frightened as the alligator had been at the strange sounds.

"Nothing but the roasting chestnuts," answered Jacko the monkey. "They are bursting and making noises like guns because the fire is so hot, and because I forgot to make holes in the nuts to let the steam out. But it is a good thing I did, for they burst and scared the alligator."

"Indeed, they did," agreed Curly.

"And we'll roast some more chestnuts in place of the burst ones," said the monkey, and he did, and Curly had as many as he wanted, and some to take home. Soon he arrived at the piggie-house, and every one was glad to see him and the chestnuts, and that's all to this story.

But in case the pretty Red Cross nurse with the blue eyes and the jolly laugh says that it's all right for the trolley car to jump over the house and play tag with the chimney, I'll tell you next about Baby Pinky and the doctor.

STORY XII

BABY PINKY AND THE DOCTOR

One night, in the piggie house where Mr. and Mrs. Twisty tail lived with their three children, there was a crying noise.

"Hey! What's that?" asked Curly, one of the piggie boys, as he threw some of the straw from his bed over on the one where his brother Floppy slept.

"Oh, I don't know. Cats howling, I guess," answered Flop. "Go to sleep and don't mind 'em."

So he and Curly tried hard to go to sleep again, but you know how it is, sometimes, the more you try to close your eyes, and dream, the wider awake you get. It was this way with the two piggie boys, though you can hardly blame them for not sleeping, as the crying noise sounded louder and louder.

"That isn't cats," said Curly, after a while.

"No," agreed Flop. "I guess it isn't. Sounds more like Baby Pinky crying. I wonder what's the matter?"

"Let's get up and look," suggested Curly who always liked to be doing something, even at night. So the two piggie boys crawled softly from their beds and looked out of the door. They saw in the next room their papa scooting around in his bare feet, carrying a kettle of hot water, and then they heard

Howard R. Garis

their mamma saying:

"There, there now, little one. Your pain will soon be better. Don't cry and wake up the boys."

"Oh, we are awake!" exclaimed Curly through the open door of his room.

"What's the matter?" asked his brother. "Is somebody sick?"

"Baby Pinky is," answered Mrs. Twistytail. "But go to sleep. We'll call you if we want you." The two piggie boys saw their papa getting more hot water, and other things, from the kitchen, and they heard their mamma walking around with their baby sister, and they tried to go to sleep, but they didn't rest much, for they were too anxious.

During the night they managed to doze off, but still they heard noises through the house, and when it was almost morning, but when the stars were still twinkling, they heard their papa go softly out of the front door. And they heard their mamma say: "Tell the doctor to come as soon as he can, Archibald." You see, Mr. Twistytail's first name was Archibald. And he answered:

"Yes, I'll get him soon," and then the two boys heard their papa sort of blowing his nose hard and coughing, as if he had a bad cold. You see, papa pigs feel as badly when their little children get sick as real papas do, every bit.

Now in the morning, when the sun was up, there was a busy time at the pig-house. First came Grandfather Squealer, the oldest pig of them all, and he was a very nice gentleman.

"You boys must be very good and quiet," he said to Curly and Flop. "For your little sister is very sick, and may have to go to the hospital."

"What's a hospital?" asked Curly.

"It's a place where they make sick folks get well," answered Grandfather Squealer. "Now, you boys get ready for school. The doctor is still here, and may be for some time."

And so Dr. Possum was - up in the room looking after poor sick Pinky. There was something the matter inside her - I didn't know what it was, but anyhow she had to go to the hospital to have it fixed, just as when the clock doesn't go, the jeweler has to put new wheels in it, or fix the old ones.

"But I don't want to go to the hospital," squealed Pinky, when they told her she would have to. "I want to stay home," and she made such a fuss that Dr. Possum said:

"This isn't good for her. We must get her to be more quiet, or she will be very ill."

"Oh, please let us try to get her quiet," begged Curly, who, with his brother, heard what was said. "We'll do some funny tricks, and stand on our tails, and sing a little song, and then Pinky will want to go to the hospital."

"Very well," spoke Dr. Possum, so the two piggie boys did all the tricks they could think of, from whirling around on the ends of their tails to rolling themselves down a hill, like a hoop, with an apple in their mouths. As Pinky watched them, she felt a little better, and when the big ambulance automobile came to take her to the hospital she was almost laughing.

And even when she got in the nice big hospital, so clean and neat, she wasn't frightened, for the little squirrel nurses were so kind to her and they looked so pretty in their caps and blue dresses that Pinky felt sure she was going to like it there. And then the doctor said to her.

"Now, Pinky, little girl, I will have to hurt you the least bit, but no more than I can help, and after it is over you will be all better and you will have no pain and you will be well. Are you going to be a brave little piggie and stand for it?"

"Ye - yes," faltered Pinky, but when the time came for them to really make her better, and when it hurt, she cried out:

"Oh, dear! Oh, dear! Oh, dear!" and she wiggled so hard that the nurses and doctors could hardly hold her, just as when some children get vaccinated.

"This will never do," said Dr. Possum. "If she doesn't keep quiet we cannot make her get well."

"I can't!" cried Pinky. "I can't! I can't!"

Well, no one knew what to do, until just then Uncle Wiggily Longears, the old gentleman rabbit, came along, and he saw at once what was the matter.

"I'll fix it!" he exclaimed. "If Curly and Flop will stand outside the hospital and sing funny songs while the doctor is fixing Pinky, she will not mind it in the least."

"We'll try it," said Dr. Possum. So the two piggie boys began to sing funny songs under Pinky's window. They sang about the mousie who had a rubber nose, and every time he blew it he bounced on his tiptoes. Then there was another one about a doggie, who could not wag his tail, because he'd fastened on it the monkey's drinking pail. And when Pinky heard these songs she felt much better, and she let the doctor do whatever he had to do to her.

And when he hurt her quite badly (though, of course, he did not mean to, for it was to make her better), and when Pinky cried, Curly and Flop danced harder than ever and sang about the kittie who had a penny hat, and when the ribbons all fell off she gave it to a rat.

Pinky laughed at that, and when her two brothers chased after Sammie Littletail, the rabbit, and made him jump over a telegraph pole just for fun, she felt so jolly that Dr. Possum could finish making her all better, and she never cried once again.

So this shows you that even little animal children can go to the hospital and not mind it at all, though I hope none of you boys and girls ever get ill enough to have to go. And in a short time Pinky was all better, and she was glad she had let the doctor do what he had to.

So on the next page, in case the baking powder doesn't shoot the sponge cake in the bathtub and make the towel ring the bell, I'll tell you about Curly and the big apple.

STORY XIII

CURLY AND THE BIG APPLE

One day, oh, I guess it was about a week after Baby Pinky went to the hospital, something else happened to the two piggie brothers. And, as most of it happened to Curly, I have named this story for him, though Flop had a part in it.

When her piggie boys came home from school one afternoon Mrs. Twistytail said to them:

"I wonder if you don't want to go to the store for me?"

"Of course we do mamma," spoke Curly as quickly as ice cream melts on a hot day.

"Certainly," added Flop, and the funny part of it was that the two brothers had just planned to go off in the woods and play soldier and Indian after school.

But as soon as they heard that their mamma wanted them to go on an errand for her, they at once made up their minds that they would go to the store first and play afterward.

"What do you want, mamma?" asked Curly. "Is it a cake of milk chocolate, because if it is -"

"We'll help eat it," finished Flop quickly with a laugh.

"No, all I need is some cornmeal to make pancakes with in the morning," spoke the pig lady. "Run along now, but you need not hurry back, and you may play on the way."

Curly and Flop whistled through their noses at hearing this, for they knew they could have some fun after all, and away they started for the store. The old gentleman duck who kept it, and who was a forty 'leventh cousin to Grandfather Goosey Gander, wrapped the cornmeal in two separate bags, so that Curly could carry one, and Flop the other.

"That will make it even," said the store duck, as he gave the piggie boys each a sweet cracker.

Back home they started, playing tag, and hide the acorn, and all such games like that, including one called "Please Don't Pull My Tail and I Won't Pull Yours." That's a very funny game.

Well, all of a sudden, as Curly and Flop were going along, they came past a field where a kind old rat gentleman was picking his apples off the trees. There were many of the apples, and they had to be put in barrels and brought into the cellar.

"Oh, don't those apples smell good," said Flop as he leaned over the fence and looked at them.

"Indeed they do," agreed Curly. "They remind me of apple pie and cheese."

Then the rat gentleman looked up, saw the piggie, and said:

"Come in, boys, and you may each have one apple. Help yourselves."

"Thank you, very much," spoke Curly. "Come on!" he cried to his brother Flop, "we'll each take a big apple, and there will be enough for a pie when we get home."

"Oh, but we can't carry big apples, with the bags of meal," said Flop. "I'm going to take a middle-sized apple."

"Well, I'm not. I'm going to take the largest I can find in the field," declared Curly, and he went hunting for a specially large one.

Of course, in a way, it was all right to do this, for the rat gentleman had told them to help themselves, but you just wait and see what happens.

Curly picked out a very large apple - the very biggest one that grew on the trees, but Flop was content with a smaller one. Then the piggie brothers started for home again.

Curly had hard work to carry the big apple and also his bag of corn meal, and first he would have to put one down to rest his legs, and then put down the other to rest his paws. But Flop could easily carry his middle-sized apple and the meal. Finally Curly said:

"Flop, can't you help me?"

"I'm afraid not," answered his brother, "though I would if I could. But I have all I can do to take care of my apple and the meal. Why don't you get a smaller apple?"

"Because I want the big one," said Curly quickly.

Well, he was staggering along with the big apple and also his bag of cornmeal, but his brother was going along much more easily, when, all of a sudden, out from the bushes sprang the fuzzy fox.

"Ah ha!" he cried. "This time I have good luck! Here are little pigs to make roast pork, and they have with them the apples for apple sauce. Oh, joy is me! Now for a fine dinner!"

With that he made a grab for both the piggie brothers, but

they managed to jump away. Off ran Flop with his middle-sized apple and the cornmeal, and after him came Curly, only he could not go so fast because his apple was so big.

"Wait! Wait!" begged Curly of his brother.

"I can't!" was the answer. "I'll send a policeman back to help you. But if you will let go of the big apple you can easily run away from the fox, for he is old, and not a good runner. Drop the apple."

"No, indeed!" cried Curly. "I want the biggest one I can find!" So he held tightly to the apple, and also to the cornmeal, and on he ran, but the fuzzy fox was getting nearer and nearer, and almost had him.

"I've got you!" suddenly snapped the fox. "I'll have roast pork and apple sauce tonight all right!" and he was just going to grab Curly and the apple and bag of meal, when out from the bushes jumped Uncle Wiggily Longears, the old gentleman rabbit.

"Here!" he cried to the fox. "You stop chasing Curly, and go home to your den!" and with that Uncle Wiggily stuck out his rheumatism crutch, and tripped up the fox so that went tumbling head over heels, and when he got up he was so lame that he could not chase even a snail for more than a week.

"Run! Run!" called Uncle Wiggily to Curly and the little piggie boy did run, and, after some trouble, he got safely home with his big apple and the meal, but Flop was there ahead of him.

"After this," said Uncle Wiggily, when he came up to the piggie house, "after this, Curly, don't take such a large apple, and you can run better when a fox chases you."

"I'll be careful after this," promised the piggie boy, and I guess he was. Anyhow it was a good lesson to him. And that night he

Howard R. Garis

and his brother had cornmeal pancakes with apple sauce on, and Uncle Wiggily stayed to supper.

Now in case the automobile tire doesn't jump into the frying pan, and pretend it's a sausage for the lady in the purple dress to eat, I'll tell you next about the piggie boys and the pumpkin.

STORY XIV

THE PIGGIES AND THE PUMPKIN

"Well, well!" exclaimed Mrs. Twistytail, the pig lady, as she went to the cupboard and looked in. "Whoever would have believed it?"

"Believed what, mamma?" asked Pinky, the little baby pig, who had been in the hospital, but who was now much better.

"Why, there isn't a bit of bread for supper!" went on Mrs. Twistytail. "And your papa will come home from the office so hungry as never was! Oh, my! I must run right out to the store and get a loaf."

"Can't Curly or Flop go?" asked the baby pig, as she looked to see if her hair ribbon was on crooked, but it wasn't. I'm glad to say.

"They aren't here," said the mamma pig. "I guess they must be off playing football, or seeing if there is any ice on the skating pond."

"Then let me go, mamma," suggested little Pinky. "I'm sure I could ask for a loaf of bread and carry it home, too."

"No, you are quite too small," said the pig lady. "I'll go myself to the store and I'll ask Mrs. Goosey Gander, next door to come in and stay with you."

Howard R. Garis

But she didn't have to do that, for a few minutes later in came Curly and Flop, the two nice boy piggies, and they were just as glad as could be to go to the store for their mamma.

Well, they started off all right, and soon they were at the bread store, where the baker cat wrapped up a nice loaf in pink paper and they started for home, going as fast as they could, so as to be there before their papa came to supper.

And, what do you think? Just as they reached the spot where stood the old stump, with the knobs growing on the side of it, like warts on a toad's back, they heard a voice saying:

"I wonder what I shall do with it? It is quite too large to cook, and I have no little boys to give it to. I think I must let it roll down hill into the pond."

"Who is that speaking?" asked Curly of his brother.

"I don't know," said Flop Ear, "but it sounds like the kind rat-gentleman who gave us the apples."

"That's just who it is," said the voice. "And who are you, if I may ask?"

"Two piggie boys," was the answer. "Can we help you?"

"Well, I have here a very large pumpkin," was what the rat gentleman said. "It is too large to cut up into pies, and I thought maybe some one might like it to make a Jack o' lantern of. Would you like it?"

"Indeed we would!" cried Flop. And Curly said the same thing.

So the nice old rat gentleman called the two piggie boys into his farmhouse and he gave them the pumpkin.

Oh! so big as it was! I'm sure I never could tell you what a fine, large pumpkin he gave to Curly and Flop. The one that was turned into a coach for Cinderella was very small along side of this.

"What shall we do with it?" asked Flop Ear.

"Make a lantern of it, of course," said his brother. "We can scoop out the insides, and cut the eyes and nose and mouth, put a candle in it, and have a lot of fun."

"All right," said Flop, "we'll do it."

So they tied a string around the pumpkin and lifted it between them, each one carrying his share. And the loaf of bread was put on top, where it would not fall off.

Well, the piggie boys had not gone very far, carrying the pumpkin home to make a Jack o'lantern, when, all of a sudden, out from behind a lot of bushes, jumped a big wolf. Isn't it funny how those bad creatures seem to always bother the piggie boys? Every once in a while something is happening to them.

I can't help it. I wish I could, but you know I have to write things exactly as they happen. Anyhow, out from behind the bushes jumped the wolf, and as soon as he saw those sweet, tender little piggies he exclaimed:

"Oh joy! Oh, happiness! Oh, appetite! Now is my chance! I shall certainly grab those two piggies and carry them off to my den."

And he chased after Flop and Curly.

But, as luck would have it, they heard him coming, and they started to run with the big pumpkin and the loaf of bread. Still the wolf came closer and closer.

"I'll have you in a few minutes!" he cried.

"I believe he will!" exclaimed Flop. "What shall we do?"

"What can we do?" asked Curly, as he helped his brother to jump over a stone, and lifted the pumpkin at the same time. "What can we do?"

"Why not make a Jack o'lantern of the pumpkin and scare the wolf?" suggested Flop. "Some of our friends did that once."

"We haven't time," said Curly. "If we stopped to make a Jack o'lantern the wolf would catch up to us and grab us. I'll tell you what to do. Let's scoop out a hollow place in the pumpkin and get inside it. Then the wolf won't see us."

"Good!" cried Flop. So he and his brother ran on as fast as they could to get far ahead of the wolf. Then they stopped for a minute, and, with their sharp hoofs, they cut the top off the pumpkin. Then, with their digging noses, they dug out the soft seeds, and soon the pumpkin was all hollowed out, so they could jump inside.

"Get in!" cried Curly to Flop.

"What about the loaf of bread?" asked his brother.

"Never mind that. We can get another. We must get away from the wolf," cried Curly.

So they jumped inside the pumpkin, and only just in time, for the wolf came rushing down the hill. But Curly and his brother wiggled themselves inside the pumpkin, and away it rolled down toward the piggies' house. The wolf saw the loaf of bread on the hill, and he thought sure the piggie boys were near it. So he made a grab, but he did not get them.

For of course they were inside the pumpkin, rolling over and over, like a rubber ball down hill. The wolf chewed up the bread, and then he saw the rolling pumpkin. Then he happened to think:

"Perhaps the pigs are inside that!" After it he ran, but it was too late, for by that time the piggie boys were safely at home. Into their front yard rolled the pumpkin, off flew the top, and out they jumped to tell their papa and mamma and baby Pinky all about it.

And Grandpa Goosey Gander loaned Mr. Twistytail a loaf of bread for supper. As for the wolf, he ran back up the hill as mad as anything about the way he had been fooled, and ever after that he never ate any pumpkin pie.

So that's all there is to this story, but in case the new brick chimney doesn't fall down in the rice pudding and make the trained nurse wild because her doll carriage has no wheels, I'll tell you on the next page about the piggie boys in the corn field.

Howard R. Garis

STORY XV

THE PIGGIES IN A CORNFIELD

One day - oh! I guess it must have been about two grunts and a squeal after Curly and Flop, the two piggie boys, had the adventure with the pumpkin - something else happened to them. In the first place, they had to stay in after school.

Now, please don't get worried, nor think anything bad of them on that account. They did not have to stay in because they whispered in class, or anything like that. No, they stayed in to help their teacher clean off the blackboards, but when they got out all the other animal children were gone.

"Come on, let's run," suggested Flop, "and maybe we can catch up to them."

"I wish we could!" exclaimed Curly, "for Jackie Bow Wow, the puppy dog, borrowed my pencil and forgot to give it back."

So the two piggie boys ran as fast as they could, but they could see nothing of the other animal children - not even little Jennie Chipmunk, who could not go very fast, for every time she saw any dust on a stone or a tree stump she used to stop and brush it off with her tail. She was so neat and clean, you see, and as she had to stop quite often, on account of there being so much dust, she couldn't go fast at all.

But, as I said, Curly and Flop couldn't even catch up to her, which shows you that they had stayed in after school for quite some time.

"Oh! they'll all be home long before us," said Curly after a bit, sitting down on a stone to rest.

"I guess so," agreed his brother, as he made his two ears stand up straight and then flop down again. "But never mind, I think you can get your pencil from Jackie Bow Wow tomorrow."

"Yes," spoke Curly, and then they went on a little farther until they came to a corn field. The corn was all cut down, and stood in big bunches, called shocks - not the kind of shocks you get from an electric battery, though, but corn shocks.

"Oh, let's take a short cut through the corn field," suggested Curly. "Maybe then we can get ahead of the others."

"All right," said Flop. "We'll do it." And, though they had never gone through this corn field, because it was owned by a cross old alligator gentleman, they now started to crawl under the fence. Just as they were inside the field they heard a little voice crying:

"Oh, dear! What shall I do. Oh, my poor tail!"

"What's that?"' asked Flop in alarm.

"I don't know," answered Curly. "Maybe it's the bad old fuzzy wolf."

"Let's hide!" exclaimed Flop, and they were looking for a place to hide when they happened to see a poor little girl mouse near a shock of corn, and her tail was held fast by a stone that had fallen on it.

"Was that you crying?" asked Flop.

Howard R. Garis

"It was," said the mousie girl. "Oh my poor tail! How can I ever get loose?"

"We'll help you," spoke Curly. "We'll root up the stone with our strong noses, and then you'll be all right."

"Of course we will," agreed Flop. "Oh, how glad we are that you aren't a wolf," he added, and then he and Curly, with their noses which were made stretchy like a rubber ball, soon had the stone off the mousie girl's tail, and she was all right, except that her tail was sore. But when her mamma could put some salve on it that would be all better, too.

"Oh! I can't tell you how thankful I am to you," said the mousie girl to the piggie boys. "Some day I will help you."

"Ha! Ha!" laughed Flop. "How can a little mousie girl like you help us two big boys?"

"Hush!" exclaimed Curly. "It isn't polite to laugh when any one offers to do you a favor, even if they are little. Besides, maybe she MIGHT be able to help us some day."

"Of course," spoke the mousie, and she felt rather badly because Flop Ear had laughed.

"Oh, excuse me!" exclaimed Flop. "I didn't mean to. I'm sure I hope you can help us, little mousie."

So the two piggie boys went on through the corn field, hoping they wouldn't meet the cross old alligator man, who owned it, and who didn't like animal boys. And the mousie went on her way.

"I think we'll soon catch up to the others," said Flop after a bit.

"I guess so," agreed Curly. "And when we do - -"

"Hark!" suddenly exclaimed Floppy. "Some one is coming!" Curly heard it, too, and he stopped talking. He looked around the corner of a stone and whispered:

"It's the old alligator man himself. What shall we do?"

"Run!" exclaimed Flop. "Run as fast as we can."

So he and Curly started to run but my goodness me sakes alive and a postage stamp! No sooner had they gone ten steps than the cross old alligator man saw them, and after them he came as fast as he could crawl on his four legs, wiggling his humpy tail. "Oh, he'll get us, sure!" wailed Floppy.

"Run faster!" urged Curly.

Well, they both ran as fast as they could, squealing with fright, and the alligator man was coming right after them, and he had almost caught them when, all of a sudden, a little squeaky voice called out:

"In here, boys! Crawl right in here, under this shock of corn, and he can't see you!"

They looked, and there, in front of a sort of cave, that was made in one of the upright piles of corn, stood the little mousie girl who had been pinched by the stone on her tail.

"In here!" she cried. "Quick, before he comes, and he won't know where you have gone!"

"But he'll know we're hiding in the corn," said Flop.

"Quick! Get inside and talk afterward!" said the mousie girl. "Besides there are so many piles of corn that the alligator man won't know which one you're hiding in, and it will take him all night to peek into them all. And after dark I'll show you the way home."

Howard R. Garis

So into the shock of corn crawled Curly and Flop pulling a lot of stalks behind them to close the hole, and they were only just in time, for, an instant later, up rushed the alligator man. Of course he could not see the piggy boys, and he was much surprised.

"But I know they're hiding somewhere!" he growled. And it all happened just as the mousie girl said. The alligator man peeked in nearly all the corn shocks, but he didn't happen to look in the one where Curly and Flop were hiding. And pretty soon it was dark, and then the piggies came out and the mousie girl showed them the way home, and the alligator man did not get them. So, you see, the mousie helped the piggie boys after all.

And next, in case the salt cellar doesn't hide in the pepper caster and make believe it's a mustard plaster I'll tell you about Flop having a tumble.

STORY XVI

FLOP HAS A TUMBLE

"Come boys!" called Mamma Twistytail, the pig lady, one morning, to her two little boys, Curly and Flop. "Come, hurry, or you'll be late for school!"

"Oh, I guess we have time enough," spoke Flop, as he looked around for the football he and his brother had been playing with. "It's early yet."

"No, it isn't," answered his mamma. "Our clock is slow by your papa's watch. Hurry now, I think I hear the bell ringing!"

"All right," answered Curly. "Come along, Flop." You see, he sometimes called his brother Flop, for short. So they kissed their little sister, Baby Pinky, good-by, and went on to school.

As they hurried along, they met Jackie Bow Wow, the puppy dog boy, and Curly said:

"Oh, Jackie, where is my pencil you borrowed?"

"Here it is!" cried Jackie, turning a somersault, as he used to do in the circus, and he handed the pencil to Curly on the end of his nose - Jackie's nose I mean.

"We chased after you last night, when we got out of school," explained Curly, "and we had a dreadful adventure in the corn

Howard R. Garis

field with the alligator man," and he told his doggie chum all about it, just as I wrote it for you in the story before this one.

So Jackie, and Curly and Flop hurried along together toward the school, when, all at once, they came to a nice, big, slanting cellar door, just right for sliding down, and on it was a sign which read:

"NO ONE MUST SLIDE DOWN
THIS CELLAR DOOR!"

"Now isn't that queer," said Jackie Bow Wow.

"It certainly is," agreed Curly.

"I wonder why no one is allowed to slide down," spoke Flop. "It's a dandy door for sliding. I've a good notion to try it."

"No, you mustn't!" said his brother. "We are almost late for school now."

"Oh, but I would just love to slide down it," went on Flop, sort of hanging back, while his brother and Jackie went on ahead. "I wonder if a giant lives under that door, or a fairy?"

"Maybe that's the reason no one must slide down it," went on the little piggie boy. But no one answered him and, though he looked all around the cellar door, he could see no reason why he should not slide down it.

"Maybe it's got slivers in, and they'd stick in me," went on Flop, as he came closer to the door, but it was as nice and smooth as heart could wish.

"Well, this is certainly queer," said Flop. "Here is the nicest sliding cellar door in all the world and no one is allowed to slide down it. I wonder who lives in the house," and he looked up at the house to which the cellar door belonged, but it was all closed up, and shutters were over the windows.

"I guess no one is at home," thought the little piggie boy.

"Say, aren't you coming to school?" called back Jackie Bow Wow, for he and Curly were some distance down the street by this time.

"Yes, come on, or you'll surely be late," said Flop Ear's brother.

"I'm coming!" cried Flop, but he thought he would take just one more look at the sliding door.

"I would like to have just one slide on it," he said. "I believe I'll try it."

He looked ahead to where his brother and Jackie were and decided that if he did take one slide he could run and catch up to them, and not be late.

"Here goes;" said Flop, and he laid his books down on a clean stone.

Then he read the sign once more:

"NO ONE MUST SLIDE DOWN
THIS CELLAR DOOR!"

"I guess it's only a joke," decided Flop. "Now for one good slide and then I'll go to school."

So he went around to the side of the door, where there was a stone, and, by stepping on this, and giving a little jump, the piggie boy got to the top part of the sliding door, ready for a coast down.

Of course he had no sled on which to slide, but his trousers were good and thick, and he knew he could not wear a hole in the seat just this once. So he gathered his legs together under him, gave himself a little push and down the slanting door he went as nicely as an icicle in the middle of the Fourth of July.

"Wow! This is great!" cried Flop. "I guess the other fellows will wish they'd taken a slide. This is nifty!"

I don't know myself what "nifty" means, but Flop said it, so I have to write it down.

Faster and faster he slid down the cellar door. It was a long one, and now he was half way to the bottom.

"Oh, won't we have fun sliding after school!" the little piggie boy cried. "I don't see why they looked rather sorrowfully after her brothers and put up that sign not to slide. This is the best cellar door I ever saw."

Faster and faster he slid, laughing and shouting in glee, and he was almost at the bottom and he was wondering if he would have time for just one more coast before school, when all of a sudden:

"Crack! Slam! Smash! Ker-bunk!"

Right down through the cellar door fell poor Flop, and down the cellar steps into a tub of water. Into that he went ker-splash! For, you see, the cellar door had broken with him and let him right through, almost half way to China, it seemed.

Into the tub of water went Flop, getting wet all over. But he managed to crawl out after a while, and as he stood there, shivering, in the cellar, looking up at the broken door through which he had fallen, a nice little old rat lady came out of the house, and, looking at Flop, said:

"Dear me! What a terrible accident. Too bad! Did you hurt yourself, little piggie?"

"N-no-not much," answered Flop. "But I - I'm all wet."

"So I see," said the rat lady. "But I thought there was a sign on the door, telling no one to slide down."

"So there was," admitted Flop, "but I didn't see why it was there, so I slid anyhow."

"I put the sign there because the door was so rotten that I knew the first one who slid down it would fall through," said the rat lady. "And to think, some one did fall!"

"Yes'm," said Flop, "I fell."

"Well, don't do it again," said the rat lady, "and tomorrow I'll have a new cellar door made. Now let me dry you off."

So she kindly did, but Flop was late for school. And - well, I suppose it couldn't be helped, even if he had to stay in. But on the next page, in case the mousetrap doesn't catch the cheese by the tail and make it squeal, I'll tell you about Mr. Twistytail's lost hat.

Howard R. Garis

STORY XVII

MR. TWISTYTAIL'S LOST HAT

"Hey, Curly can you be out?" called Peetie and Jackie Bow Wow, the puppy dogs, as they stood in front of the piggie boys' house one morning when there was no school. I forget whether it was Saturday or because the owl lady school teacher had to go and take her music lesson.

Anyhow, there was no school, and as Peetie and Jackie stood in front of the pig house and called:

"Hey, Curly! Hey, Flop! Come on out!"

"Of course we will!" cried Curly. "What are you going to do?" and he and his brother hurried with their breakfast and ran out in the yard.

"Let's play football game," suggested Jackie, "like we did the other day."

"No, let's go off in the woods and play camping out," suggested Curly.

"Yes, that will be more fun," added Flop, and then the two puppy dog boys thought the same thing, so off to the woods they started.

"I wish I could go," said Baby Pinky, as she their chums.

"Never mind, Pinky," said Mrs. Twistytail. "I'm going to bake pies, and I'll make a specially little one just for you."

"Oh, goodie!" cried Pinky, and then she went out in the yard to play in her go-cart. Pretty soon along came Jennie Chipmunk and she played with Pinky, so the little pig girl didn't mind so much, after all, that her brothers had gone away.

But now let us see what happened to Curly and Flop, to say nothing of Peetie and Jackie Bow Wow. On and on they went through the woods, and pretty soon Jackie found a nice juicy bone, and Peetie found a bit of meat, while Flop found an ear of corn and his brother picked up a big turnip.

"Oh, joyfulness!" exclaimed Flop. "Now we can have a lunch in the woods, just like real camping out!" And so they did. Under a tree, on the soft leaves that floated down from the branches above, with a flat stone for a table, and sticks for knives and forks, the piggie boys and their chums ate their lunch and had lots of fun. Then Curly said:

"Now let's play soldier," and so they did, with sticks for guns, and when the boy animals called out: "Boom! Boom!" and "Bang! Bang!" it sounded as real as anything.

Well, they were running around in the woods, shouting and laughing and making believe they were soldiers at war, when all at once, just as Curly passed in front of a hole that seemed to go away under ground, he saw something roll out. It was something round and black and hollow, and at first the little piggie boy thought it was a big black stone. But, when he looked a little closer, he saw that it was a hat - a man-pig's hat - just the kind they always wear.

"Oh, Flop! Oh, fellows! Come here!" called Curly. "See what rolled out of the hole under this old tree."

Of course, they all came running up at that, and stopped

playing soldier, and they gathered around the hat.

"Whose is it?" asked Jackie Bow Wow.

"Where did it come from?" inquired Peetie, making his tail go round like a pin wheel.

"It's our papa's hat!" suddenly cried Flop. "I can tell because it's got his initials inside," and, surely enough there were the letters "A.T." inside the hat, standing for "Archibald Twistytail."

"Our papa's hat!" exclaimed Curly. "Is it possible?"

"Of course, it is," said Floppy, as he picked it up. "Papa has lost his hat."

"But it rolled out of that hole," said Curly, "and it isn't lost, for we have found it."

"Then if papa's hat came out of that hole, our papa must be in there," said Flop.

"Why, of course," agreed Jackie Bow Wow.

"But what is he doing in there?" asked Curly, "and what sort of a place is it? I can't see him," he added, as he stooped down and tried to look into the hole.

"I don't know what he's doing in there," said Flop, "but I know what sort of a place that hole is. It's a wolf's den, and the wolf has our papa, Most likely he's eating him now, and he threw the hat out because he couldn't chew it - the wolf, I mean."

"Oh!" cried Curly, jumping up and down, he felt so badly.

"Oh; oh!" barked Jackie Bow Wow.

"Oh! oh! Double Oh!" growled Peetie Bow Wow. "What shall we do?"

"We must get him out of there!" exclaimed Flop as quickly as a rubber band can play the "Annie Laurie" song. "There are four of us here, and we have our wooden guns. I guess we are a match for one wolf. We must save our papa."

"Of course!" agreed Curly, bravely.

"But how?" asked Jackie Bow Wow.

"Listen," said Flop, just like a telephone girl.

"A wolf always have two doors to his den - a back one and a front one. This is the front one - where our papa's hat rolled out. Now, Jackie, you and Curly go to the back door, and make a noise like a soup bone. The wolf will think some company has come to supper with him, and he'll run to the back door. As soon as he gets there, Jackie, you bark like anything, and, Curly, you fire off your wooden gun."

"But what will you do?" asked Curly of his brother.

"Peetie and I will stay at the front door," said Flop. "As soon as we hear you making the noise we'll rush in the den by the front door and get papa and help him out. Then we'll all run away."

Well, every one thought that was a fine plan, and they did just as Flop said. The wolf came rushing to his back door when he heard the noise there, and maybe he wasn't surprised to see Curly and the puppy dog! Then Flop and Peetie rushed in the front door, and there, inside the den, they found poor Mr. Twistytail tied to the table leg.

"Quick!" cried Flop. "Bite the ropes, Peetie." And the puppy dog did, and Mr. Twistytail was free. "Now, come with us!" cried Flop, and he and his papa and Peetie ran out of the wolf's den just in time, for the bad creature, seeing he had been fooled at his back door, rushed up to bite the pig gentleman.

But he was too late, that wolf was, for the piggie boys and their papa and the puppy dog boys got safely away, and the wolf didn't dare follow because he was afraid of the wooden guns. Then when they were all safe home, including the hat, Mr. Twistytail told how the wolf caught him as he was coming back from work, and how his hat accidently rolled out of the den. And if it hadn't been for the hat maybe Mr. Twistytail would not have been saved.

Anyway, he was not hurt a bit, and in the next story, in case the bicycle doesn't roll over the egg basket and make an omelet out of the pin cushion, I'll tell you about Mamma Twistytail's new bonnet.

STORY XVIII

MOTHER TWISTYTAIL'S NEW BONNET

"Archibald," said Mrs. Twistytail, the lady pig, to her husband at the breakfast table one morning, "I think I shall have to have some money today."

"Money? What for?" he asked. "Do the children need new shoes, or have we no more coal left?"

"No, I want the money for myself," said the pig lady. "I need a new bonnet, and I am going down town this morning and get it at the five and ten dollar store."

"Very well," said Mr. Twistytail, good-naturedly, so he put his foot in his pocket and took out a lot of money, which he gave to his wife. Then he kissed Baby Pinky, and Curly and Flop good-by and went to work in the phonograph factory where he put the squeaks in the wheels.

"Oh, if you are going shopping for a new bonnet, mamma!" exclaimed Flop, "may I come with you?"

"Yes, and may I?" asked Curly, as he spun around on his front paws like a top under a Christmas tree. "And if you have any money left, mamma, after getting your bonnet, maybe you will buy us each a hot ice cream soda,"

"Oh you boys!" cried Mrs. Twistytail with a laugh. "No, I am

Howard R. Garis

afraid I can't take you two with me, for it is Baby Pinky's turn. You boys had a nice time the other day, playing in the woods, when you saved your papa and his hat from the wolf's den, and so now it is Pinky's turn to have some fun. I'll take her shopping with me."

"Oh goodie!" cried Baby Pinky, and she jumped into her go-cart and out again, making the springs jounce up and down like anything.

"But I'll give you and Flop each a penny," said Mrs. Twistytail to Curly, "and you can buy some corn candy with sour milk on top."

That pleased the boy piggies very much, and they ran off to school with their pennies, while Mrs. Twistytail got ready to go shopping after her bonnet with Baby Pinky. Pretty soon they went down town and in the five and ten dollar bonnet store.

"Have you any bonnets?" asked Mrs. Twistytail.

"Indeed I have," said the nice lady frog who kept the store. "I have all kinds of bonnets," and then she sang a little song that went something like this, to the tune "High diddle-diddle:"

"I've bonnets of ribbon, and bonnets of paper,
I've bonnets both red, white and blue.
Some bonnets of leather, for cold stormy weather,
And bonnets of feathers and glue.

"I've bonnets becoming, and some that are stunning;
I've bonnets to wear upside down.
And if you will try one, I'm sure you will buy one,
To go with your new party gown."

"I'm sure I will, too," said Mrs. Twistytail, as the frog lady finished and made a little bow to the looking-glass. "You may show me the blue one," she went on, and frog lady did.

"Oh, mamma! That is lovely!" cried Baby Pinky. "But I think one with more flowers on would be nicer."

"I think so, too," spoke the pig lady, and so she bought a bonnet with a lot of flowers on it that looked as real as those which grow in the woods and fields. Then Pinky and her mamma started for home, Mrs. Twistytail wearing her new bonnet.

"We'll take the short cut through the woods," said the pig lady when they had alighted from the trolley car on which a nice toad gentleman was the conductor, because he could hop on and off so quickly, and not step on any one's toes.

So through the woods went Mrs. Twistytail and Pinky, and they had not gone very far when, just as they got to the wolf's hollow log den out of which Mr. Twistytail's hat rolled that day, up sprang the bad, impolite old animal himself and grabbed the pig lady and her little daughter.

"Ah, ha! Now I have you!" cried the wolf. "Your husband got away from me, Mrs. Twistytail, but I have you, and you can't get away, and I have Pinky, too!" and he held them both tightly, in his paws.

"Oh, please let us go!" begged Pinky.

"No," growled the wolf, sticking out his red tongue because he was so hungry.

"Oh, do!" pleaded Mrs. Twistytail. "I'll give you all the money I have left from shopping if you'll let us go."

"No! No!" answered the wolf, more growlier than before. "You have none left. Besides money is no good to me - I can't eat money!"

"Oh, mercy!" cried Pinky. "Are you going to eat us?"

"Indeed I am," said the wolf, smacking his jaws, and then Pinky and her mamma tried as hard as they could to get away from the wolf, but they could not. Holding them tightly in his paws, the wolf started for his den, and, seeing Mrs. Twistytail's new bonnet, he took it off her head, roughly like, and said:

"And I can't eat this! I guess I'll throw that away, as I did your husband's hat. But no one will see it and come to rescue you as they did him."

"Oh, my lovely new bonnet!" cried Mrs. Twistytail, and Pinky felt so badly that she cried. But you just wait a minute and see what happens to that bad old wolf.

The wolf was just going to toss the bonnet, all covered with almost real flowers as it was, away up in a tree and just about to carry the pig lady and Pinky down into his den, when, all at once, there was a buzzing sound in the air and a voice cried:

"Ah, ha! Here are some flowers. Now we can get some honey!"

"Indeed we can," said another voice up in the air. "It is rather late for such blossoms, but I am glad we saw them in time. Come on, now, everybody, get the honey!"

And with that a whole swarm of stingery honey bees flew down from the sky toward Mrs. Twistytail's flowered bonnet that the wolf held in his paw. You see, the bees thought the flowers were real and that they could gather honey from them.

And then, just as Pinky saw the bees, she had an idea and she cried out:

"Oh, dear little bees! That is my mamma's new bonnet, and the wolf has caught us. Please sting him and make him let us go!"

"Don't you dare sting me!" growled the wolf. "Take the bonnet if you wish, but don't touch me," and he threw the bonnet to one side.

Some of the bees alighted on the bonnet, and as soon as they found that the flowers were not real they got quite angry. And they thought the wolf had played a trick on them, so they flew at him, and stung him on his nose and tail and eyes and lips and even on his tongue, until he cried out with pain and fright. Then he let go of Pinky and her mamma and ran down into his den, and the pig lady was safe. The bees never stung them once, but were very kind to them, and with their wings brushed the dirt off Mrs. Twistytail's bonnet so that it was as good as new.

Then the bees flew away, Mrs. Twistytail and Pinkey went safely home, and the wolf had to stay in his den for a week and put witch hazel on his stings.

So that's all tonight, if you please, but next, in case the kitchen stove doesn't go out on the porch and play hide-and-seek with the hammock, I'll tell you about Curly and the sour milk.

STORY XIX

CURLY AND THE SOUR MILK

"Oh, mamma!" exclaimed Curly the little piggie boy, as he rushed into the house one noon and nearly upset his little sister Pinky, in her new go-cart. "What do you think? There isn't going to be any school for two weeks!"

"Why not?" asked Mrs. Twistytail, who was just getting dinner.

"Because the schoolhouse roof blew off in the storm last night," said Flop, who was Curly's brother, "and it will take two weeks to put a new one on. So the nice owl lady teacher said we could have a vacation. Oh, I'm so glad!"

"My goodness me, sakes alive and some Montclair caramels!" cried Mrs. Twistytail. "A school vacation this time of year - so near winter. I never heard of such a thing."

"But it will be all the nicer," said Curly, "and we can go after chestnuts every day. Hi-yi! Hurrah!" and he squealed and jumped around the room, and so did Flop, and they were the two most delighted little pigs you ever saw. Just then along came Uncle Wiggily Longears, the old gentleman rabbit.

"What's this!" he cried. "What is going on here?"

"No school!" squealed Curly. "No school! We have a vacation!"

"The very thing!" suddenly said the old gentleman rabbit. "I was just wishing it was summer time, so some of my animal friends could come away with me. I am going on a little vacation trip myself, and I thought I would have to go alone. But if there is no school, then Curly and Flop can come with me."

"Where to?" asked Flop.

"To Raccoon Island in Lake Hopatcong," answered Uncle Wiggily. "We'll go up to my bungalow, stay two weeks and have a good time."

"Oh, fine!" cried Curly.

"Oh, joyousness!" squealed Flop, as he spun about on one leg and tickled Baby Pinky with the other.

Well, that afternoon, Mamma Twistytail got the two boys ready, and off they went with Uncle Wiggily to Raccoon Island in Lake Hopatcong, which is a very nice place. It was beginning to get dark when they arrived, and, after they had eaten some candy, and Uncle Wiggily had opened the bungalow, he looked around and said:

"Now, boys, you will have to go to the store for something for supper."

"What shall we get?" asked Flop.

"Well, see if you can get a cabbage or a turnip for me," spoke the old gentleman rabbit, "and for yourselves whatever you like. Here is the money."

"I want some sour milk," spoke Curly, for you know piggie boys like sour milk as well as you do sweet.

"And I want a corncob cake," went on Flop.

"Very well, go down to Pop Goes the Weasel's store and get it," said Uncle Wiggily, and the two boys started off to the other end of the island, where Pop Goes the Weasel kept a grocery store. Flop got his corncob cakes first, and as Curly had to wait for the milk to get sour he said to his brother:

"Now, Flop, you hurry back with Uncle Wiggily's cabbage and carrots, and I'll soon come with my sour milk."

"Won't you be afraid?" asked Flop, for the woods were now quite dark.

"Afraid! Nonsensicalness no!" exclaimed Curly, "and a boquet of wild flowers besides. Run along."

So Flop ran back toward the bungalow, and pretty soon Pop Goes the Weasel said the milk was sour enough, and he gave it to Curly in a pail.

Through the dark woods went the little piggie boy, and he had not gone very far before he heard some one crying, and a voice saying:

"Oh, dear! I'm lost! I can't find my bungalow, and I can't find my motorboat, and I'm afraid - dreadfully afraid!"

"Ha! I wonder who that can be?" thought Curly Tail. "Perhaps it may be the bad alligator trying to scare Cora Janet. No, that can't be," he went on, "for Cora Janet is down in Montclair, making funny music tunes on the piano."

Then he heard the gentle little crying voice again, and he knew it was somebody in trouble, Curly did, and he called out:

"Who is there?"

"I am," sobbed a voice.

"And who are you?"

"My name is Ethel Rose," went on the voice, "and I am lost. Oh, please help me. I'm so afraid!"

"Of course, I'll help you," spoke Curly bravely. "But why is your name Ethel Rose? - that is two names."

"I don't know," answered the little girl, and then she stepped out from the bushes where she had been crying, and the moon shone down on her face and her ear-rings and dark hair, and Curly said:

"Now I know why they call you Ethel Rose."

"Why?" she asked.

"Because you are as pretty as a rose," and at that Ethel laughed. "But come," went on Curly, "I'll show you the way to our bungalow, and then Uncle Wiggily will take care of you."

"Oh, will he?" cried Ethel Rose, and so she walked along beside Curly, who was carrying his pail of sour milk. And, all of a sudden, when they were near the bungalow, there was a rustling in the bushes, and out jumped a big black bear.

"Ah, ha!" the bear cried. "Now I have you Curly, and you, too, Ethel Rose! Oh, how nice! You come with me and I will tell your fortune!"

"But I know my fortune already," said Ethel Rose, and she was just ready to cry again, for she did not like bears.

"Never mind, come along to my den, anyhow!" growled the bear. "I am going to have roast pork for supper!" and he made a grab for Curly and Ethel Rose, and caught them in his big claws.

And then, all at once, he saw the pail Curly was carrying - that

Howard R. Garis

bear did - and he growled out:

"Ha! Ha! What have we here? Something good, I'll venture. Well, I'll take that first!" And before Curly could stop him the bear tipped up the pail and drank every drop of sour milk at one mouthful! And then! Oh, dear!

"Wow! Woof! Snickery-snee! Bur-r-r! Lemons! Vinegar! Sourgrass!" cried the bear. And his mouth was puckered up so from the sour milk - just as when you eat lemons if you have the mumps - that the bear couldn't open his jaws to take even one bite. And Curly knew this, so he cried:

"Come on, Ethel Rose, we can get away now! Uncle Wiggily will save us!" So Curly Tail helped Ethel Rose to run away and the bear's mouth was so puckered up from the sour milk that he had to run down to the lake to get a drink of water, and so Curly Tail and pretty Ethel Rose got safely to the bungalow and away from the bear. And that's all there is tonight, if you please.

But the next story, in case the marshmallow doesn't stick on Ethel Rose's hair ribbon, and make a pin cushion of it, will be about Flop and the pie lady.

STORY XX

FLOP AND THE PIE LADY

Uncle Wiggily Longears, the nice old gentleman rabbit, and the two piggie boys, Flop Ear and Curly Tail, were sitting on the porch at the bungalow at Raccoon Island, Lake Hopatcong, wondering what they could do next for their autumn vacation fun. Curly was trying to take some snapshot photographs of a little red squirrel, who was jumping down across the cot beds, all in a row like soldiers, and Flop was wondering whether he could catch any fish.

"Well, we must do something," said Uncle Wiggily. "It isn't every day you boys get a vacation after the regular summer one, so you must enjoy it."

"We wouldn't have gotten it if the roof hadn't blown off our school," said Flop, "and, as long as we're here, I say let's go off in the woods and look for chestnuts."

"All right," said Curly, and they were just going to leave the bungalow, when, all at once, there was a rustling in the bushes and out came - no, not a bear or a wolf, or even a bad skillery-scalery alligator, this time. No, it was a nice lady, with real soft, brown hair, and the jolliest whistle you ever heard!

What's that? You didn't know ladies could whistle? Well, this one could, and play the piano at the same time. Out she came from the bushes, and she said:

Howard R. Garis

"Oh, Uncle Wiggily, I'm so glad to see you and the two little piggie boys."

"Well, we are glad to see you, too," said Uncle Wiggily, politely making his best bow, "but I'm afraid I don't know you."

"Oh, yes, you do," said the lady. "I make pies, and if you like I'll make one now."

"Will you, really?" cried Flop. "Oh, I would dearly love an apple pie, with a bit of sour milk cheese."

"Then you shall have it," said the lady, as she trilled out a little tune by whistling until it sounded like a bird in the lilac bush. "Have you any apples?" she asked, puckering up her lips.

"Yes!" exclaimed Flop. "Here they are!" and he brought out a basketful. The lady said they would make a lovely pie, so she rolled up her sleeves, and spoke, saying:

"Now, I am sorry, but I would like you all to leave the bungalow. You, Uncle Wiggily, and you, also, Flop and Curly. For when I make apple pies I get all kerslostrated - which means fussed - if any one is around. So kindly run away, and when you come back the pie will be ready for you."

"All right; we'll go," said Uncle Wiggily. "I'll go pull my motorboat up on dry land, so it won't get caught in the ice when the lake freezes this winter, and you boys can help me."

So Curly and Flop went off to help Uncle Wiggily, and the pie lady - for such they called her - started her baking. She peeled the apples and cut them up, and then she got the piecrust mixed. Uncle Wiggily had already built a fire so she did not have to do that. And all the while she whistled and whistled, until it made you feel glad and happy just to hear her. And when you smelled that apple pie baking - well, say! I mustn't write any more about that, or I'll want to put my typewriter down cellar, and go out hunting for the lady myself.

Pretty soon Flop, who was helping Uncle Wiggily with the motorboat, sniffed the air, grunted once or twice, and said:

"I smell something good! I guess I'll go see what it is."

"All right," said Curly, who was quite tired from having assisted his rabbit uncle to haul up the boat. "I'll stay here, Flop, and when you find the good thing that you smell, bring me some."

So Flop promised, and he kept sniffling away, and the lovely smell grew plainer and plainer as he moved toward the bungalow, until he exclaimed:

"Ah, I know what it is! The pie lady! Oh, I wonder if the pie is done?"

Nearer and nearer he went to the bungalow, and he heard a whistle, and then he saw the pie lady bustling around with a long apron on, and Flop asked:

"Is the pie done?"

"Almost, little piggie boy," she answered.

"You may wait for it to come out of the oven. How old are you?"

"Seven," said Flop, and then he asked the lady.

"What is your name?"

"Margaret," she answered. "Margaret More."

"More what?" asked Flop.

"More pies, I guess," laughed the pie lady as she whistled

again, this time just like a canary trilling when it swings at the top of its cage in the sunshine. Curly laughed, too, and then the lady went to the oven to take out the pie.

And, would you ever believe it if I didn't tell you? No, I'm sure you wouldn't. But, anyhow, all of a sudden, out from the bushes came a bad, fuzzy old wolf, and he stood in front of the bungalow, crying:

"I smell apple pies! I smell apple pies! Also a little piggie boy! Oh, what a fine lunch I am going to have!"

Well, Flop was so frightened that he couldn't even walk, much less run, and all he could do was to squeal, "Oh dear!"

The pie lady heard him, and came running to the door of the bungalow.

"What is the matter?" she asked, and then she saw the wolf.

"Oh, my!" she exclaimed. "What shall I do?"

"Nothing!" exclaimed the wolf, sticking out his red tongue. "I'll do all that's necessary. But first I'll eat the apple pie, and then I'll carry you and Flop off to my den!"

Well, when Flop heard that - heard that the wolf was going to eat the lovely pie - he became real brave, that little piggie boy did.

"You shan't have that pie!" he cried.

Then the wolf, with a big jump, started for the bungalow to get the pie and the pie lady, but what do you think Flop did? He just grabbed up the pan of apple peelings - long, curling peelings they were - and he threw them at the wolf! Right at the bad creature's legs he threw them, and the apple peelings tangled up in the wolf's fur and in his tail, and his legs and paws, and head-over-heels he went, falling down on the ground and bumping his nose on a hard stone.

"Oh, wow! Oh, woe is me! Oh too-badness!" growled the wolf, and he ran away to his den to get some salve to put on his bumped nose, and so he didn't get the pie lady, nor the pie, nor Flop, either, at least not that day.

Then the apple pie was done, and the pie lady whistled a nicer song than ever, and Curly and Uncle Wiggily came to the bungalow and they all ate pie and were as happy as happy could be. But, as for the wolf, the less said about him the better.

So on the next page, in case the door-knob doesn't tickle the dining room bread-board and make the sawdust come out of the breakfast oatmeal, I'll tell you about the piggie boys and the jelly.

Howard R. Garis

STORY XXI

THE PIGGIES AND THE JELLY

One day, when Curly and Flop, the two piggie boys, had been at Uncle Wiggly's bungalow on Raccoon Island for some days, the old gentleman rabbit said to them:

"Now, boys, I have to go down to the store, kept by Pop Goes the Weasle, to see about some butter and things for supper. Will you be afraid to stay here alone?"

"Indeed we will not!" exclaimed Curly.

"Not even if the bad fuzzy wolf comes out of his den after more apple pies?" asked the rabbit gentleman.

"Not even then!" exclaimed Flop. "If he does, I'll throw more apple peelings at him, and trip him up so that he bumps his nose again."

"Good!" exclaimed Uncle Wiggily, as he limped off on his red, white and blue rheumatism crutch. "And if the apple pie lady comes whistling along again, get her to make us a prune pudding," he said.

"We will," promised the piggie boys, and then they began to play games in front of the Lake Hopatcong bugalow, while Uncle Wiggily went to see Pop Goes the Weasle, who kept the grocery store.

"Well, I guess she isn't coming," said Flop, after a while.

"Who?" asked Curly.

"The pie lady. I do wish she would, for I am hungry," and he looked at the bushes, and, all of a sudden, they began to rustle, and the piggie boys didn't know whether to run away or stay there.

"Maybe it's the pie lady," said Curly.

"Yes, and maybe it's the bad black bear," suggested Flop. "I'm going to run into the bungalow!"

Well, he was just going to run, and Curly was going to follow, when, all at once, a sweet gentle voice said:

"Oh, dear, I'm sure I'll never find any! Oh, and I want it so much! I wonder where I could get any?"

The two piggie boys looked, and there they saw an Indian maiden coming out of the bushes. They knew she was an Indian maiden because her hair was in two long braids, hanging down in front of her, and she had a brown dress on, and she was very beautiful, just like a picture.

"We needn't be afraid of her," whispered Curly to his brother.

"No indeed," agreed Flop. "I wonder what it is she is looking for?"

"Jelly," answered the Indian maiden, who heard what the piggie boy asked. "I am looking for a jar of jelly. Oh, I just love jelly, and I haven't had any in so long that I forget how it tastes! Since early morning I have been traveling looking for jelly, but I can't find any. Some wild bees offered me honey, but I would like jelly. Have you any?" and she looked at the bungalow,

"Why, I think we have some," said Curly politely.

"I'll go look!" exclaimed Flop, for they were both anxious to do some kindness for the Indian maiden, whom they liked as soon as they saw her. She was not a wild Indian, you know, but the kind that lives in Montclair, maybe; a tame one.

So Flop ran in the bungalow to look for the jelly and Curly picked a nice bunch of flowers for the Indian maiden, and she put them in her hair and looked prettier than ever.

"Here is the jelly!" cried Flop, coming out with as much as he could carry. "I'm sure Uncle Wiggily would want you to have it," he said, and then he gave the Indian maiden a spoon and she began to eat jelly and was as happy as anything.

"Oh, that is very good!" she exclaimed. "I hope some time I can do you piggie boys a favor for being so kind to me." So she ate all the jelly up - that is, all that was good for her - and she was just going away, having thanked Curly and Flop, when all at once, on a sudden, out from behind a tree came the big black bear. He waved his paws in the air, and, wrinkling up his black nose, he growled out:

"Ha! I smell jelly! I'm going to have some, too, to eat on my roast pork!" and he looked hungrily at the two piggie boys. They were both too frightened to move, but the Indian maiden was brave.

"Come! Come! Give me that jelly!" growled and grumbled the bear! "Then I'll take you piggie boys off to my den and make the Indian maiden cook you."

"Oh, but I'll not do it!" said the Indian maiden whose name was Pocohontas. "I like Curly and Flop, for they were kind to me and gave me jelly."

"Well, then, I want jelly, too!" growled the bear. He made a jump, intending to take the jelly away from the Indian maiden, but Curly and Flop cried out:

"No, you don't! Get away from here at once, you bad bear."

"Well, if I go, I'll take you with me!" said the bear. "If I can't have jelly I'll have you piggie boys!" and he caught one of them under each paw.

"Oh, help!" cried Curly, trying to get loose, but he could not.

"Save us! Save us!" begged Flop, making his tail spin like a pinwheel.

"I will save you!" called the Indian maiden.

"Oh, if I only had a bow and arrow I would shoot the bear and rescue the two piggie boys! I know what I'll do. I'll make a bow and find an arrow."

So she took a bent branch of a tree for the bowf and for the string she used some strands of her long braids. But the needed an arrow, and all the while the bear was carrying Curly and Flop off to his den.

"I know!" cried the Indian maiden. "A hat pin! My very longest and sharpest hat pin! That will do for an arrow!"

She ran to where she had left her hat in the bushes when she was looking for the jelly, and quickly got a hat pin. This she shot at the bear from her bow.

"Whizz!" it went through the air, hitting the bear on the end of his soft and tender nose.

"Oh, wow!" he cried. "Oh, woe is me!" and his nose pained him so that he dropped Curly and Flop and back to the bungalow ran the piggie boys as fast as they could. And the bear went off to put some cooling mud on his nose, where the hat pin had hit him.

Howard R. Garis

So that's how the Indian maiden saved the piggie boys from the bear, and they gave her more jelly and thanked her, and then, using a long thorn instead of a hat pin, which the bear carried off in his nose, Pocohontas went off looking for more jelly, and Curly and Flop went to asleep.

And next, in case the horse radish doesn't jump over the oysters and scare them so they fall into the clam chowder, I'll tell you about Flop and the marshmallows.

STORY XXII

FLOP AND THE MARSHMALLOWS

"Boys," said Uncle Wiggily Longears, the old gentleman rabbit, to Curly and Flop, the piggie chaps, one morning. "Boys, do you think you can get along by yourselves this afternoon?"

"Why, I guess so," answered Curly, as he looked off across the beach at Raccoon Island in Lake Hopatcong. "But where are you going, Uncle Wiggily?"

"Oh, Pop Goes the Weasel wanted me to come down to his store and have a game of Scotch checkers after dinner," said the old gentleman rabbit. "He says he is lonesome since all the summer folk went away."

"Of course, we can get along all right," spoke Flop. "We'll have our lunch and, we'll do the dishes, so you can go and play Scotch checkers with Pop Goes the Weasel."

"But what are Scotch checkers?" asked Curly.

"Oh, when you play that game," said Uncle Wiggily, "you have a nice Scotchman standing near you all the while to cook Scotch scones over a hot fire. And scones are good to eat; something like pancakes, with maple syrup on, only different. It is fun to play Scotch checkers."

"I should think so," said Flop. "And could you bring us a few scones, Uncle Wiggily!"

"I'll try," said the old gentleman rabbit, "though Pop Goes the Weasel and I are very fond of eating them when we play checkers."

So in the afternoon Uncle Wiggily went to visit his friend at the store on Raccoon Island, and the two piggie boys stayed home to keep house. And, when they had washed the dishes, Curly said:

"Now, Flop suppose we go looking for adventures. I'll go one way and you can go the other, and we'll see who can find an adventure first."

"All right," said the other little piggie boy. So they started away from the bungalow. But as Curly fell asleep before he had gone much farther than the Sylvan Way (which is a nice little rustic bench on the island) no adventure happened to him. But wait until I tell you what happened to Flop.

Off he started, and he had not gone very far before he heard some one crying out:

"Oh, what shall I do with them? Oh, so many as there are! I never can eat them all!"

"My!" exclaimed Flop, "I wonder if that is a bad bear who has caught a whole lot of piggie or rabbit children? Who ever it is can't eat them all, so it must be something extra good. I wonder what it is?"

So he hid behind a stump, and after a bit he peeked out and there he saw his old friend, little Cora Janet, of Montclair, walking around in the woods with a big box in her arms. And on the box was a sign which read:

CANDY

"My gracious sakes alive and some lollypops!" exclaimed Flop. "She has so much candy she doesn't know what to do with it! I wonder if I can help her?"

So Flop jumped out from behind a bush, made a low bow, and said, most politely:

"Can I help you, Cora Janet?"

"Oh, yes, you can!" she exclaimed. "You see I came up here looking for the Indian Maiden who likes jelly so much. I thought I would give her some of my marshmallows, as I have a whole box full-many more than I can eat. But I can't find the Indian Maiden – Pocohontas - and now I shall have to eat all the marshmallows myself."

"Why?" asked Flop, curious like.

"Because," answered Cora Janet, "because there is a big bear chasing after me. He smells the sweet candy and he is so hungry that he will want to eat the marshmallows and me, too. But if I could only get rid of the candies he might let me alone. Oh, what shall I do? I've toasted them, and roasted them and eaten them just as they are out of the box, and put them in a cake and everything, but still the bear chases after me!"

"Of course I do!" suddenly growled a voice in the bushes and just then out popped the bear. The hat pin which the Indian maiden had shot in his nose was out now, and that bear was as angry as anything. He wanted to grab Cora Janet and take her off to his den I guess. Anyhow he growled as angry as could be!

"Oh, what shall I do!" called the little girl. "How can I get rid of all these marshmallows, for if the bear takes them it will only make him the more hungry and then he will want to eat me, and you too, Flop."

"That must never be!" exclaimed the little piggie boy. "Ha! I have it!" he cried. "We will throw the marshmallows at the bear, and make him so stuck up that he won't want ever to eat anything again except pepper-hash!"

"Good!" cried Cora Janet. So she and Flop opened the box of marshmallows. Just then the bear made a rush for them, intending to grab them both in his big, long claws and carry them off to his den.

But Flop threw a sticky marshmallow candy, and it landed in one of the bear's eyes and stayed there.

"Oh, wow!" cried the shaggy creature, and he could only see out of one eye. Then Cora Janet threw another marshmallow and it closed up the bear's other eye. Then he couldn't see at all.

"Oh, wow again! Double wow!" cried the bear. Then, as fast as they could throw them, Flop and Cora Janet tossed the sticky marshmallow candies. They stuck up the bear's nose so he couldn't hear, and got in his ears so he couldn't smell. Oh! just listen to me, would you! I'm so excited that I got that part wrong. But, anyhow, the bear couldn't see, nor smell, nor hear. And then more marshmallows got in his mouth, and they were like sponges, and he couldn't even bite any one, for they stuck on his teeth like gum. Then Flop said:

"We are safe now, Cora Janet, and we have enough marshmallows left to roast at the camp fire tonight."

And so they had. And that bear was so stuck up with the soft marshmallow candies - in his eyes and nose and mouth and ears and paws and tail and fur - that he had to go to sleep in the lake for a week and a day to get them washed off.

So he didn't bother Cora Janet nor Flop any more, and pretty soon Curly awakened and came back to the bungalow to hear about his brother's adventure. And Uncle Wiggily came back from playing Scotch checkers with Pop Goes The Weasel, and everybody was happy, even Cora Janet, and they had roast marshmallows for supper.

And on the next page, in case the little boy across the street doesn't slide down the front steps and scare the milkman's horse so that it drinks up all the ice cream, I'll tell you about the piggie boys and the big fish, and it will be a Hallowe'en story.

STORY XXIII

THE PIGGIES AND THE FISH

On the morning of the day when it was to be Hallowe'en, Curly Tail, and Flop Ear, the two piggie boys, awakened in Uncle Wiggily's bungalow, on Raccoon Island in Lake Hopatcong, and Curly Tail whispered:

"What are you going to dress up like, Flop Ear?"

"Oh, I guess I'll make believe I'm a loaf of bread. What are you going to be?"

"An apple pie," said the other little piggie boy, "I'll stick apples all over myself, and some bits of pie crust, and when we get through playing Hallowe'en we can eat them."

"Fine!" cried Curly Tail. "I wish I was going dressed up like an ice cream cone, but then I'd melt so fast I wouldn't have any fun. So I guess I'll be a loaf of bread."

"And we'll fool Uncle Wiggily, won't we?" said Flop Ear.

"We surely will," declared his brother. But if they could have looked into the next room, and have seen Uncle Wiggily laughing to himself, and winking his eyes, and rubbing his leg that had rheumatism in it - well, maybe those piggie boys wouldn't have felt so funny.

"Fool me, eh? Will they?" whispered Uncle Wiggily. "We'll see about it," and then he hopped about on his crutch to help the boys get breakfast.

"We must have all the good times we can," said the old gentleman rabbit, "for soon the new roof will be on your school and you will have to begin studying your lessons again. Be happy while you're here, for soon the snow will fly and the ice will come, and we will have to go away from the lake."

"Oh, we're going to have a good time, Uncle Wiggily," said Curly Tail, or Curly, as I often call him for short, and then he looked at his brother, and they both laughed and pretended it wasn't anything at all. But Uncle Wiggily knew better.

"Well," said the old gentleman rabbit, after breakfast, "I guess I'll go down and play Scotch checkers with Pop Goes the Weasel. You boys can stay here, but if the bad alligator or the fuzzy fox tries to get you, just call for me."

"All right," said Curly Tail, and when his uncle was out of sight he and his brother began to dress up for Hollowe'en, which is the night everyone puts on false faces you know.

One of the piggie boys made a lot of flour paste, colored with brown sugar, and that was to fix him so he would look like a loaf of bread. And Flop Ear made himself look like an apple pie.

"Now, we'll just practice, ready for tonight, when we're going to fool Uncle Wiggily," said Curly Tail, and they did, having lots of fun.

Just before supper Uncle Wiggily came home from having played Scotch checkers with Pop Goes the Weasel. The old gentleman had something under his coat, but when Curly Tail and Flop Ear asked him what it was he only laughed and said:

"Oh, you'll soon see!"

Well, it got pretty dark, and Curly Tail and his brother thought it was time for them to dress up and play a trick on their uncle. So they took their false faces, one like a lump of buttered bread and the other like a piece of cheese, and went out in the woods to dress. They intended to come and knock on the bungalow door and see what Uncle Wiggily would do and say when he saw them.

Pretty soon they were both ready, and, really, if I do say it myself, Curly Tail looked just like a ten-cent loaf, with flour in his buttonhole and all that, only he didn't have any real butter on, as that was so greasy. And Flop Ear, or Flop, or Floppy, for short, looked too cute for anything - just exactly like an apple pie, and he even carried a bit of cheese to go with it, and a toasting fork.

"Now, we'll fool Uncle Wiggily," they said, as they started for the bungalow. But they didn't know what had happened to the rabbit gentleman. They hadn't gone very far before, out in a boat on the lake, not far from shore, they heard a voice calling:

"Oh, help! Help! He's such a big one that I can't get him in, and Percival has fallen overboard! Help! Help!"

"My goodness! What's that?" asked Curly Tail, in surprise.

"Some one must be in trouble," said Flop Ear. "Let's see who it is."

"But it might be the bad skillery-scalery alligator, with the lumps on his tail," said the other piggie boy. Then Flop Ear looked out on the lake, where it was all lighted by the moon and he said:

"I see a lady in a boat. Surely she would not harm us. And she spoke of Percival - she must mean the old circus dog! I am going to see what is the matter!"

"Better not! Maybe it's a trick to catch us!" said Curly Tail.

But just then a lady on the lake called again: "Oh help! He is such a big one that I can't get him into the boat, and Percival has fallen overboard!"

Then there was a great splashing, and a rustling in the bushes and Flop Ear called:

"We're coming to help you, lady! What have you got that is so big?"

"A fish," she answered. "My husband, Percival, is a great fisherman and he caught the biggest fish in all the lake, but it pulled him out of the boat. However, I have hold of the pole and line, and the fish is still fast to the hook. Oh, help me to catch him!"

So the piggie boys said they would, and they ran down to the shore, and the lady in the boat passed them the pole. Then Curly and Flop pulled as hard as they could, and old circus dog Percival scrambled out of the water, and he helped pull, too, and, all of a sudden, from the bushes along the edge of the lake - on dry land, but not in the water - there suddenly flopped the biggest fish any one had ever seen.

"Oh, what long ears the fish has!" cried Curly Tail, when the moon shone on the fish. "I never saw a fish with ears!"

"I'm not a fish," said a voice. "Oh, please let me go. The hook is caught in my collar. Please let me go!"

"Who are you?" asked Percival, in wonder.

"I'm Uncle Wiggily Longears," was the answer. "I dressed up like a Hallowe'en fish to fool Curly Tail and Flop Ear. I was walking along the shore in the dark, thinking I could catch the piggie boys, when, all of a sudden, something caught in my coat collar, and I was dragged through the bushes. I was choked so I could hardly speak, and I didn't know what had happened to me."

Howard R. Garis

"Oh, that's too bad," said Percival. "I guess I happened to catch you on my fishhook by mistake, when I was tossing it around. But why are you all dressed up?" he asked Curly Tail and Flop Ear and Uncle Wiggily.

"Because it is Hallowe'en," said Flop Ear; "but I guess we have had enough of it."

"Yes," said Uncle Wiggily, "come up into the bungalow and we will duck for apples, eat marshmallows and have fun."

So Curly Tail took off his bread crumbs clothes, and Flop Ear his apple pie suit, and Uncle Wiggily his fish scales, and they all took off their false faces, and Percival and the lady whose name was Gertrude, had a good time.

And in the next story in case the ash can doesn't roll off the roof and fall on the dog house to scare the puppy cake I'll tell you about Curly Tail and the little afraid girl.

STORY XXIV

CURLY AND THE AFRAID GIRL

One day, when Uncle Wiggily, the nice old gentleman rabbit, went down to the store on Raccoon Island, in Lake Hopatcong, kept by Pop Goes the Weasel, there was a letter there for Curly Tail and also one for Flop Ear.

"I wonder who can be writing to the piggie boys," said the rabbit gentleman. "I'll take the letters to them."

So he stopped to play just one game of Scotch checkers with Pop Goes the Weasel, only they didn't quit finish it because Mr. Pop's cat jumped on the middle of the board to catch a mosquito and scattered the checkers all over.

"Scat!" cried Pop Goes the Weasel. "Why did you do that?"

"Never mind," said Uncle Wiggily. "She didn't mean to."

And really the cat didn't mean to, and the mosquito got away after all, and Pop Goes the Weasel began picking up the checkers, but the rabbit gentleman said:

"I'm afraid I can't stay to finish the game. I must get back with the letters for Flop and Curly," calling them thus for short.

"Very well," said Pop, "and take them some sour milk chocolate candy with my best wishes, for the letters may be

Howard R. Garis

from home, telling them to come back to school."

And really, that is just what the letters said. They were from the nice owl lady school teacher, saying that the roof was back on the school now, and that in a few days all the animal children must begin reciting their lessons again.

"Well, then, we must have all the fun we can the few remaining days that we are to be on Raccoon Island," said Flop Ear.

"Correct," spoke Curly Tail. "Let's take a walk and see if we can find an adventure."

So off they started from Uncle Wiggily's bungalow, and when they came to a place where there were two paths through the woods, Curly Tail said:

"Now, Flop Bar, you go one way and I'll go the other, and we will see who first meets with an adventure."

"Very well," agreed Flop Ear, and off he went through the woods, but, as nothing happened to him except that he fell down a well and had trouble getting out again, I shall not tell his adventure. Instead, I will relate what happened to Curly Tail.

On and on he went, and he was wondering what would happen to him, when, all at once, as he came to a little river that flowed through the island, he heard a voice saying:

"Oh, I shall never get across. I know I shan't. I'm so afraid of water, and I know there are cat-tails and pussy willows and all sorts of things like that around here. Oh! what shall I do? I want to get across to see my grandmother, but how can I?"

"Hum! That is queer," thought Curly Tail. "I wonder who that can be? I had better be careful, though, for it may be the fuzzy fox trying to fool me."

So, carefully hiding himself behind a stone, he peered over the top, and once more he heard the voice saying:

"Oh! isn't it dreadful to be afraid!"

"Why, it's a little mousie girl," exclaimed Curly Tail out loud.

"Of course, it is," said the little creature beside the river. "And I'm afraid of the water, and the cat-tails and the pussy willows and all that."

"There are no pussy willows out now, they only come in the spring," said Curly Tail. "Though there may be some cat-tails. But they are not real cats, you know. They won't hurt you. Are you a little afraid, mousie girl?"

"Yes, but that isn't my name," she said. "My name is Edna, and I'm dreadfully afraid of the water. How shall I get across?"

"I'll get a big board and make believe it is a boat," said Curly Tail. "Then you won't be afraid."

"Oh, yes, I will," she said. "Can't you think of some other way?"

Curly Tail shook his head, and even twisted up his ear, and then he thought real hard.

"I have it!" he cried. "You shall get on the board boat, and all the while you must keep looking up at the sky. Then you will not see the water, and you'll think you're flying and you won't be afraid."

"The very thing!" cried Edna, the little afraid mousie girl. So Curly Tail got a nice, big board for a boat, and pushed it into the water. Then he got a pole to shove himself and the mousie girl across the river, and they both got on the boat.

"Now mind!" exclaimed Curly Tail. "Keep looking up, and

you won't be afraid."

Off they started, and Edna wasn't much afraid. When they were about halfway across, and she felt real glad that she would soon see her grandmother, she said:

"Oh, I guess I'm brave enough to look at the water now. I think I'm not afraid with you, Curly Tail."

"All right," spoke the little piggie boy, and he was just going to tell the mousie girl to look down if she wanted to, when, all at once, after the boat, with his big jaws open, and his tongue going over his teeth like a nutmeg grater, came the bad skillery-scalery old alligator, with a double hump on his tail.

"Oh, my!" thought Curly Tail. "If she looks down now, and sees that alligator, she'll surely be so afraid that she'll faint, and maybe fall into the water, and then I'll have to jump in to save her, and the alligator will get us both. What shall I do?"

Well, the mousie girl was just going to look down, and she would surely have seen the 'gator, when Curly Tail cried:

"Don't look! Don't look! Oh, lobster salad! don't look!"

"Why not?" asked the mousie girl.

"Because - because it's - it's a surprise!" was all Curly could think of to say.

"Oh, if it's a surprise I must surely look!" said the mousie girl. "I just love surprises!"

"I guess she won't like this kind!" thought Curly Tail, but what he said was:

"Quick! Tie your handkerchief over your eyes, and make believe you are playing blind man's bluff. Then you can't look until it's time. Quick!"

So the mousie girl, whose name was Edna, did as Curly Tail told her. She blinded her eyes, and then, the piggie boy knew she would not see the 'gator. On came the ferocious creature, ready to swallow the boat, Curly Tail and little afraid girl all at once. But Curly Tail just stuck the push pole down the alligator's throat, and that made the 'gator so angry that he lashed out with his tail, made a big wave, and that washed the boat and the piggie boy and the mousie girl safely up on shore. And then they were all right, for on dry land they could run faster than the 'gator could.

"Where's the surprise?" asked Edna, as she took off the handkerchief.

"There he goes," said Curly Tail, showing her the alligator, who was swimming away, and Edna was glad she had not seen it when on the boat or she knew she surely would have fainted. Then she went on to her grandmother's, after thanking Curly Tail, and the little piggie boy went back to the bungalow.

And on the next page, if the boys don't take my cocoanut cake for a football and roll it up hill, I'll tell you about the piggies and the dinner party.

STORY XXV

THE PIGGIES AT THE PARTY

One day a nice lady stopped in front of the house where lived Curly and Floppy Twistytail, the two piggie boys, and called to them as they were playing football in the yard.

"Is your mamma in?" asked the lady, as she looked to see if her earrings were dingle-dangling.

"Yes," replied Curly Tail, "she is. Would you like to see her?"

"Indeed, I would!" exclaimed the lady, as she blinked her two eyes and laughed in a jolly fashion.

"But she is lying down," explained Flop Ear, "so if you want to sell her some new kind of soap to make our faces clean or some baking powder that will puff a cake up like a balloon, I don't believe she wants any."

"Bless your dear little pink noses!" exclaimed the lady. "I'm not selling anything. I just came to ask your mamma if you could come to my party."

"A party?" cried Curly Tail. "Are you getting up a party for us?"

"For all the animal children," explained the lady, whose name was Sadie. "I want you all to come to my dinner party and have a good time. It's going to be away up in Montclair."

"Oh, I guess we can come," spoke Flop Ear. "Are you going to have ice cream?"

"Yes, ice cream," replied the Sadie lady, "and all sorts of good things. Uncle Wiggily will be there, and all your friends, so I wanted to ask your mamma if you could come."

"Of course we can!" cried Curly Tail. "We'll be there!"

"Very good," replied the lady whose name was Sadie. "Then I shall expect you," and off she hurried to invite some other animal children, her long earrings going dingle-dangle as she walked along, and the rose in her hair falling over sideways.

You see, Curly Tail and Flop Ear had come back from Raccoon Island at Lake Hopatcong, where they went to visit Uncle Wiggily Longears, the old gentleman rabbit, while a new roof was being put on their school in place of the one that had blown off. The piggie boys had now been back for some little time, and in a few days school would open again.

"But, before it does, we'll go to the lady's dinner party," said Curly Tail, as he combed out the bristles on his back to make them look like a paint brush.

"Indeed we will!" exclaimed his brother, and then they heard their mamma stirring about in the house, so they knew she was awake.

"Let's go ask her!" suggested Curly Tail, and in they ran to tell about the Sadie lady asking them to the party.

Their mamma said they might go, and they felt so happy that they even let their little sister, Baby Pinky, play football with them. And it would have been all right, except that when Flop Ear kicked the ball to Pinky, she couldn't get hold of it in time, and it flew up and broke Grandpa Squealer's window.

But he said he didn't mind.

Well, in a few nights, it was time for the dinner party, and Curly Tail and Flop Ear dressed in their best, with their velvet hats on their heads, started for the high part of Montclair where the Sadie lady lived.

And Oh! How nice the house looked when they got there. It was all lighted up, and there were paper roses on the piano, for it was too late for real ones, and the table was all set with nice dishes and things to eat, and all of the piggie boys' friends were there, from Sammie and Susie Littletail, to Uncle Wiggily Longears, the rabbit gentleman.

Then they began to eat, for this Sadie lady was one who loved animal children, and was always giving dinner parties, and affairs like that for them. Oh! Such good things as there were to eat, and when it was all over, and the candy and nuts were served, the Sadie lady read some poetry about a funny little lake, all made of sweet ice cream, and every time you fell in it you had a funny dream.

Then, after supper, they all sat about the fire on the hearth – Uncle Wiggily and Grandpa Goosey Gander and all the animal children, and the Sadie lady and Uncle Wiggily told ghost stories, and all sorts of other tales.

And, all of a sudden, just at the most scary part, where the big giant falls down stairs, jumps over the cot bed and scares Cora Janet's doll and Pocahontas and Ethel Rose - all of a sudden, I say, just as Uncle Wiggily got to that part, there was a noise out on the porch, and a voice cried:

"I want to come in! I must come in!"

"Oh, dear!" gasped Flop Ear.

"Who can that be?" asked Curly Tail, and he shivered so that you would have thought he was eating cold ice cream again, only he wasn't, for he was chewing on hot marshmallows.

"Let me in! Let me in!" cried the voice again.

"Oh, it's the bad skillery sealery alligator!" cried Flop Ear. "I know it is."

"Or else the fuzzy fox!" spoke Curly Tail, and just then there was a noise at the window, and they all looked up, and there stood a big black bear, tapping his paws on the glass.

"Oh, wow!" cried Uncle Wiggily.

"Sour milk and maple sugar pancakes!" yelled Grandpa Squealer, and everyone was so frightened that no one knew what to do. But the Sadie lady cried out:

"Ha! I'm not going to have a bad bear break up my dinner party in this way!" so she caught up a box of marshmallows, opened the window, and tossed the white sugar coated candies right in the bear's face.

All over him they flew, and he was so surprised that he thought it was snowing big white flakes.

"Oh, wow!" the bear cried. "Winter is here, and I must hurry back to my den before I get snowed in. I thought I was going to have a good supper, but I guess I was mistaken. Oh, woe is me! It's snowing! It's snowing!"

Then he ran down off the porch as fast as he could, and the Sadie lady called up the policeman dog on the telephone, and she hollered like anything because she was so excited.

But there was no need for the police, for the bear was so kerslostrated by the marshmallows and the powdered sugar snow flying all over him that he went and hid in his den for a week and a day, and didn't bother anyone for sometime.

Then Ethel Rose, one of the real pretty girls at the party, and Pocahontas, the Indian maid, and Cora Janet's doll and everybody else had more ice cream, and then they went home; and so did Curly Tail and Flop Ear, and the Sadie lady's dinner party was over, but every one said it was just fine, and they wanted to know when she was going to have another.

So that is all now, if you please, but on the next page, in case the sewing machine doesn't pull all the threads out of my little dog's hair ribbon, I'll tell you about Floppy and the bon fire.

STORY XXVI

FLOPPY AND THE BONFIRE

One night, after an election in Woodland, where the Twistytail family of pigs lived, Curly, one of the piggie boys, asked his brother Floppy if they couldn't have some fun.

"I guess so," spoke the other little piggie. "I have a big pile of leaves, so why can't we make a bonfire?"

"The very thing!" cried Curly Tail. "There are always bonfires after election, and we'll have ours now."

"And we'll invite all the other animal boys to help us," suggested Curly Tail. "Sammie Littletail will want to come, I know, and so will the squirrel boys, and Jimmie Wibblewobble, the duck, and the Bow Wow puppy boys."

So, as it was after school, and they had done their home work lessons, the piggie boys could run out and play. In a vacant lot, not far from their house, Flop Ear had collected a big pile of leaves, ready for the fire, and he said to Curly Tail:

"Now, if you go get the other fellows, I'll find some more leaves, and some old boxes and barrels and we'll have a fine big fire."

"All right, I will," agreed Curly Tail. So off he ran over the fields and through the woods to call all his friends to the

Howard R. Garis

bonfire which Flop Ear was going to make.

"Now for a surprise!" exclaimed the little piggie boy who was left near the pile of leaves. "I'll look for some potatoes and I'll put them to roast in the bonfire and when it is all over we'll eat them, and sit about the blaze, telling stories about the election."

So he crawled through a fence into a field near by, where there were some late potatoes, and soon, with his strong, rubbery nose, he was rooting them up. The field belonged to Grandfather Goosey Gander, and Flop knew the old gentleman goose would not mind if the boy animals took a few potatoes.

"Now to make the fire and roast them," spoke the little piggie boy, and when he had shoved the leaves all up in a heap with his nose he lit them with a match.

"Won't Curly Tail and the others be surprised when they come up, and see the fire already going?" thought Flop Ear. "And they'll be more surprised when I pull out the roast potatoes for them. Oh! I almost forgot! I must get some salt to eat on them."

Into the house he ran, with his queer little kinky tail twisting around like a piece of strawberry shortcake, and Floppy got the salt. His mamma was busy getting supper, and she did not see him, and as his sister, Baby Pinky, was practising her piano lesson on the tin dishpan, she made so much noise Mrs. Twistytail did not hear the piggie boy, so no one stopped Flop Ear.

Maybe if mamma had known that he had a bonfire she would not have liked it, and I want you children - especially you little ones - to promise Uncle Wiggily that you will never, never make a fire unless some older person is there to watch you. Fires are very bad, you know - and burns - Bur-r-r-r! How burns do hurt!

Well, anyhow, Flop Ear had his fire going, and the potatoes were roasting in the hot leaves, and he had the salt all ready to eat on them. As he came running back to the blaze, out of the shadows stepped someone, and a voice said:

"Ah ha! Good evening! I was wondering who had made this good fire for me."

"I - I did," said Flop Ear, "but I didn't make it for you. I made it for us."

"Never mind, it will do very well for me," went on the voice. "It will save me the trouble of kindling one to roast my pork sausage and chops - I mean you!" exclaimed the voice.

Flop Ear gave a jump, and looked more closely at the figure in the shadow by the fire. And then he saw that it was a big, bad old fox, with a fuzzy tail.

"Oh! Oh!" gasped the little piggie boy. "You don't mean that, do you; that you're going to roast me!"

"Exactly what I'm going to do," replied the fox, and he caught hold of Flop Ear. "We will wait until the fire is a little hotter," he said.

Oh, how poor Flop Ear did try to get loose, but he couldn't because the fox held him too tightly. And the fire got hotter and hotter, and the little piggie boy was hoping that Curly Tail and the other animal boys would come back in time to save him, but he could neither see nor hear anything of them.

"I guess I'm going to be roasted!" he cried. "Oh, if Uncle Wiggily were only here. Or even Grandpa Squealer!"

"Ha! No one will come to save you!" snarled the bad fox, and just then, what do you think? Out from the fire rolled some of the potatoes Flop Ear was roasting for his friends. Out rolled two big potatoes, and the fox, seeing them, exclaimed:

Howard R. Garis

"Ha! What have we here? Something good to eat, I should say," and he smelled the baked potato. "Oh Yum yum!" he cried, and he smacked his lips. "That will go most excellently with roast pork. I think I will eat one, and then I'll put you on the fire to cook," he said to Flop Ear.

The little piggie boy didn't say anything, but he felt very bad. And the fox, holding him with one paw, took up a roasted potato in the other, and cracked it open with his teeth.

And then - !

Well, you know how hot roast potatoes are, just out of the oven, I dare say. This one, from Flop Ear's bonfire, was even hotter. It was just roasting hot, and the fox had bitten into it.

"Oh, wow!" cried the fuzzy creature. "Oh, double wow, and some ice cream cones! Oh, pepper casters! Oh, mustard! Oh, my mouth, how it burns! And my paws!"

And then he had to let go of Flop Ear, and run to the brook to get a drink of cold water - that fox did - because the hot potato burned his mouth so, but I guess it served him right.

Anyhow, Flop Ear was free, and the next minute along came Curly Tail and all the other animal boys, and then of course the bad fox had to run away and put cold cream on his tongue. Flop Ear told all that had happened, and then the bonfire was made bigger than ever, and when the roast potatoes were cool they all ate some, and had a fine time.

So, that's all now, but in the next story, in case the pear doesn't fall off the apple tree and hit the ragman on the nose, I'll tell you about Flop Ear and the skate wagon.

STORY XXVII

FLOP AND THE SKATE WAGON

One morning Flop Ear, the little piggie boy, awakened in his bed of straw, and said:

"I don't feel very well today."

"I wish I didn't, too," spoke Curly Tail.

"Why?" asked his brother in surprise. "I'm not fooling. Honestly, I don't feel well. Do you want to be sick, too?"

"Just a little bit," answered Curly Tail. "Just sick enough so as not to have to go to school."

"Oh, that's so!" exclaimed Flop Ear. "There is school today. I thought it was Saturday, and I was sorry I didn't feel well, but now -"

Well, as it happened it was Friday, instead of Saturday, and, of course, there was school. But when Mrs. Twistytail heard that Flop Ear did not feel well, she said:

"Perhaps you had better not go today. Just lie abed and maybe you will be better by afternoon."

So Curly Tail had to go to school alone, and he felt rather lonesome, and Flop Ear stayed at home, just like the little pig

Howard R. Garis

in the story.

But pretty soon, oh, I guess about 10 o'clock, when it was too late to go to school, Flop Ear got out of bed and said:

"I don't feel quite so badly now, mother. Maybe if I go out in the air, I'll be all well."

"All right," she said, and there was a funny little twinkle in her eyes. "But first you must take some castor oil, and then I will be sure you will be better," she added.

Then Flop Ear wished he had gone to school, whether he felt well or not, but there was no help for it; he had to take the castor oil. After it was down - and it wasn't much fun swallowing it, let me tell you - after it was down, Flop Ear walked out in the street sort of slow and thoughtful-like, and wished he had someone to play with, or something to do.

"It isn't so much fun staying home as I thought it would be," he said. Just then, in an ash barrel, he saw one roller skate. It was pretty well battered and worn, but the four wheels of it were good yet, and Flop Ear, as he took it out and knocked the ashes from it, said:

"Ha! One roller skate. Now if I had two I might have some fun, and forget about the castor oil."

"You can have fun with one roller skate," said a voice behind the little piggie boy, and turning, Flop Ear saw Uncle Butter, the goat gentleman, just coming back from having delivered all his milk.

"How can you have fun with one rollar skate?" asked Flop Ear.

"By making a skate wagon," said the goat gentleman. "I saw some boy animals up in Roseville playing on them yesterday, and I'll tell you how to make one. First, you have to have a box, a long, narrow board, a stick and some nails and string."

"I can get all those!" exclaimed Flop Ear, and he did. Then Uncle Butter took the roller skate apart at the place where it slid together to be made smaller or larger. Right apart he took it, and there were two wheels on one part and two on the other.

The goat gentleman used the string to fasten two wheels on one end of the long narrow board and two wheels on the other end. Then he nailed the box on the front end of the board, right over the front wheels, and on top of the box he nailed the stick for a handle, just as on a bicycle, only this handle was straight and not curved.

"There is your skate wagon," he said to Flop Ear. "You take it to some street that runs down hill and you start at the top. Stand up on the board, near the box, and lean against it so you won't fall off. Take hold of the handles, and then push yourself off. Down the hilly street you will roll on the skate wheels, just like a coaster wagon."

"Fine!" cried Flop Ear, as he thanked Uncle Butter. Then he ran to the top of a hilly, smooth street to try his skate wagon.

He stood up in the middle of the long narrow board, took hold of the handles on top of the box, and steadied himself. Then, with one foot he gave himself a good push, and down the hill he went as fast as anything, making a noise just like a real roller skater boy only louder.

"Oh, this is great!" he cried as he reached the bottom of the hill, and ran back for another coast down it. Then Flop Ear forgot all about being sick, and he had lots of fun riding on his skate wagon, so you see that even one roller skate may be good for something.

Well Flop Ear was just going to coast down the hill for about the forty-'leventh time when, all of a sudden, he heard a voice calling:

Howard R. Garis

"Save me! Save me! Oh, help me!"

He looked around and there he saw a poor old lady cat being chased by a bad dog that had once caught Uncle Butter to pull out his horns. The lady cat was running as fast as she could with her tail all swelled up like a bologna sausage.

"Save me from the bad dog!" she cried.

"Bow-wow! Woof! Woof! Bur-r-rr!" barked the dog. "I'll get you!"

"No you won't!" cried Flop Ear. "Get on my skate wagon!" he called to the old lady cat, and with one jump she landed in the box. Flop Ear gave a good push, jumped on the wagon himself, and down the hill he went faster and faster, with the dog coming after him.

"Oh, he'll get us!" cried the lady cat.

"No he won't!" shouted Flop Ear. Faster and faster went the skate wagon down the hill, and the bad dog tried so hard to catch up to it that, all of a sudden, his legs got tied up in a hard knot - yes, sir, just as hard a knot as if a sailor had made it. And, of course, that dog turned a somersault, and went head over heels and he couldn't run any more until one of his friends untied the knots in his legs.

But by that time Flop Ear and the lady cat were safe at the bottom of the hill on the skate wagon, and the dog could not get them. Then the cat lady thanked the piggie boy very much, and gave him a penny, and Flop Ear went to school that afternoon, and was all better, and later he and Curly Tail had lots of fun on the queer wagon Uncle Butter had told how to make.

And so in case the rose bush doesn't scratch the lilac leaves off the pie plant and make the clothes line catch cold, I'll tell you next about Baby Pinkie and the lemon.

STORY XXVIII

PINKY AND THE LEMON

One day, when Flop Ear and Curly Tail were at school, Mrs. Twistytail, the pig lady, said to Baby Pinky, her little girl:

"Pinky, I am going to run across the street for a minute to ask Mrs. Wibblewobble to lend me a spool of thread. It is so chilly out that I don't want to take you along. So will you be afraid to stay here alone, just a little while?"

"No, indeed, mamma," spoke Pinky. "Why, what is there to be afraid of?" she asked with a laugh.

"Nothing in the least," replied her mother, "but sometimes little girls, and boys, too, for that matter, are afraid to stay alone, even when their mamma wants to go get a drink of water."

"Oh! I hope I'm not that kind, mamma," spoke Pinky.

"Then I'll just run across the street for a minute," went on Mrs. Twistytail. "Everything is all right here. There is nothing on the stove to boil over, but be careful not to go near the fire."

"No, I'll stay right here, mamma," said Pinky. "I'll look out of the window, and watch the leaves dancing up and down in the breeze."

Howard R. Garis

So Mrs. Twistytail went over to Mrs. Wibblewobble, the duck lady's house, and Pinky sat down to wait for her to come back. But you know how it is sometimes, when ladies get talking together, they have so many things to say, about how to make the loaf of bread last longer, and how high the butter is - so high that they have to get on a step ladder to reach it - and how boys wear out their shoes and trousers so fast and the newest way to fix your hair, and what to do when your best dress gets all spotted with ice cream, and how scarce coal is, and what a long winter we're going to have - all things like that ladies find to talk about, and it was that way with Mrs. Twistytail and Mrs. Wibblewobble.

Well, do you know, the first thing Mrs. Twistytail knew she had forgotten all about what she came after - let's see now, what was it - I declare I've forgotten myself. Just excuse me while I look back and see. Oh! I remember, it was a spool of thread.

Yes, Mrs. Twistytail got so interested talking to the duck lady about a new way to make a tight dress loose that she forgot all about the spool of thread.

"Well, mamma is staying quite a long time," said Baby Pinky after a bit, as she sat by the window. "I hope nothing has happened to her." She looked, but she could not see her mamma coming back, and then Pinky said:

"I guess I'll just dust off the piano, to keep busy, and it won't seem so long until mamma comes home."

So she began knocking the dust off the piano to the floor just as Jennie Chipmunk did it with her tail brush, and Pinky made so much noise that she did not hear the door open and some one come in. That is she did not until she heard some one walking in the room behind her, and then the little piggie girl turned around and exclaimed:

"Oh, mamma! How you frightened me."

But, oh my! when she saw who was in the room, poor Pinky was frightened more than ever. For there, with his face all swollen, stood a bad old baboon who had escaped from the monkey circus down the street.

"Bur-r-f! Ah ha! Wow! Now I have you!" barked the baboon, for they make a noise something like a dog with the chicken-pox.

"Why, why, what is the matter?" asked Pinky, never dreaming that there would be trouble, for she was such a gentle little thing. "Why is your face all swelled up?" she asked.

"I have the mumps," explained the baboon, who had a blue nose. "I have the mumps, and I am hungry. Little pigs are good for the mumps, I have been told. I guess I'll take you."

"Oh! I'm sure you must be mistaken," said Pinky, politely. "Surely you are wrong. I am not good for mumps, and I'm sure they're not good for me."

"Nor me, either," cried the baboon, putting his paw to his swollen jaw. "I don't want 'em but I have to have 'em, and, as you are the only thing that's good for them, I'm going to take you away with me. No, on second thought, I'll eat you up here and now."

"Oh, please don't!" cried Baby Pinky, and she wished, Oh! how she did wish her mamma would come back. "How did you get in here?" she asked.

"I just waited until I saw Mrs. Twistytail go out," said the blue-nosed baboon, "and then I knew you were here alone. So in I came, here I am, and now this is the end of you!"

"Oh, please don't hurt me!" cried Baby Pinky, but that savage baboon, rubbing his blue nose with the end of his tail - for he had a red tail - that baboon, I say, made a jump for Pinky.

"Oh!" she cried, as she leaped out of the way. "I'll get you something to eat, and then you won't have to take me," and out into the kitchen she ran, with the mumpy baboon after her. All Pinky saw on the table was a lemon, and, thinking the baboon might like lemonade, she caught hold of it, cut it open with a knife, and then -

Well, that baboon made a jump for her, and, as he did so, Pinky accidentally squeezed the lemon. Now, as everybody knows, when you have the mumps, if a person even says "pickles," or "vinegar," or "lemons" to you, it makes your throat all pucker up and pain you like anything, and you can't even seem to swallow. Mumps and sour things don't seem to go together.

And when the sour lemon juice got in the baboon's mouth and eyes, and some trickled down on his mumpy throat. Oh, wow! if you will excuse me saying so.

"Bur-r-! Scumpf! Fuffphmn, Xzvbgetyriep! Bfrewcript! Xvbnhytrwewqauitopekgsteredse!" cried that baboon, and no one could understand what he said, not even a phonograph, for you see his mouth and throat were nearly closed up by the puckery lemon. And of course he couldn't eat Pinky, for he could not even swallow some slippery elm, which as everybody knows, is the slipperiest thing there is.

"B-r-r-r!" cried the baboon again.

"Zyxwvutsrqponmlkjihgfedcba!" and he said the alphabet backward. Then, holding his mumpy jaws in both paws and winding his red tail around his blue nose, out of the house he ran, leaving the little piggie girl safe. And her mamma saw the baboon running away, and, without even stopping for the spool of thread, she came home and felt very badly that Pinky had been frightened.

"But you were very brave to hand the mumpy baboon a lemon," she said, and I think so, too, for it was just the right thing.

And next, in case the fire shovel doesn't burn a hole in the tablecloth and let the sugar run out and catch cold, I'll tell you about the piggies and Santa Claus.

STORY XXIX

THE PIGGIES AND SANTA CLAUS

"Oh, so many things as I have for you to do today!" exclaimed Mrs. Twistytail, the pig lady, to her two boys, Flop Ear and Curly Tail, one morning. "Such a lot of work!"

"My!" exclaimed Flop Ear. "What is it, mamma? Have we wood to chop or water to bring in?"

"Oh, neither one," said Mrs. Twistytail, with a smile, as she shook the crumbs off the tablecloth, for the family had just finished dinner. "I mean we have so many things yet to get for Christmas. There are plums to buy for the plum pudding, and the candy and nuts and oranges and figs and dates and the sour milk lollypops and everything that Santa Claus hasn't time to bring."

"Why!" exclaimed Baby Pinky, who was putting on her new lemonade-colored hair ribbon, "I thought Santa Claus brought everything."

"No, not quite everything," explained Mrs. Twistytail. "He brings all the presents, of course, but he lets the papas and mammas get the good things to eat, because different children like different things. You wouldn't like, for instance, to have nothing but hickory nuts, or walnuts, or chestnuts in your stockings, would you, boys?"

"No, indeed!" exclaimed Curly Tail and Flop Ear together, just like twins, though they weren't.

"For those things are for Billie and Johnny Bushytail, the squirrel boys," went on Mrs. Twistytail. "And they wouldn't like to have sour milk, and cold boiled potatoes, and the things that you like.

"So, as I say, there are lots of things for us to do to get ready for Christmas, and you boys will have to help me. I think today I'll send you to the store for some raisins and citron and plums and other things to make puddings and pies."

"Oh, goodie!" cried Flop Ear.

"And maybe we can clean out same of the cake and pie dishes after you get through baking," suggested his brother.

"I think you may," said their mamma.

"But what can I do?" asked Baby Pinky, the littlest pig of them all. "Can I go to the store for anything?"

"You will stay home with me," said Mrs. Twistytail, "and help me bake. Now, boys, you had better start, so as to get home before dark. Here are the things I want," and she gave them a list written out on paper.

Oh! so many lovely victuals as there were! I can't write about them, for I haven't had my supper yet, and I'm so hungry, when I think of the good things, that I might even take a bite out of my typewriter, and then I couldn't print any more stories for you, and that would be too bad for me.

Anyhow, there were many good things that Mrs. Twistytail wanted, and soon Curly and Flop were on their way to the store with a big basket.

They got them all, and they took sniffs and smells, though not

Howard R. Garis

so much as weenyteeny nibble of the Christmas things. But, oh! how they did wish the time would come when they might really eat them!

"What do you most want for Christmas?" asked Curly as he and his brother tramped on through the snow-covered woods.

"A toy steam engine," replied Flop Ear. "And what do you want, Curly Tail?"

"A make-believe automobile."

"I hope we get them," went on Flop Ear with a sigh, and pretty soon, off in the woods, they heard a voice calling:

"Whoa, now! Stand still there, if you please. Some of the things are slipping off my sleigh, and I want to fasten them on. Whoa there, reindeer!"

"Listen to that, would you now!" whispered Curly Tail to his brother, as they hid down behind some bushes.

"Reindeer!" exclaimed Flop Ear. "There's only one person who has reindeer and he is -"

"Santa Claus!" interrupted Curly Tail. "We've found Santa Claus, Floppy, and this is the best chance in the world to tell him what presents we want for Christmas!"

"That's right," agreed the other piggie boy. "We'll speak to him," and then they walked on a little farther and they saw the dear old saint himself, with his red coat, all trimmed with white fur, and his white beard, and he was as round and fat and jolly as anything.

"What ho! Hello!" cried Santa Claus, when he saw the piggie boys. "What are you doing here?"

"We are on our way home from buying Christmas things,"

said Flop Ear. "But have you really Christmas presents there, Mr. Santa Claus?"

"I have indeed," replied the jolly old saint, with a twinkle in his eyes. "But no one is allowed to see them until the right time. You see I am traveling about, measuring the sizes of different chimneys, so I can tell whether or not I can slide down them. Just as I got here some of the toys began to slip off the sleigh and I stopped to fasten them on. But I suppose you have your toys all picked out?"

"Yes," replied Flop Ear. "I want a toy steam engine, and Curly wants a toy automobile."

"Oh, my!" exclaimed Santa Claus, and his voice seemed rather sad.

"Why, what is the matter?" asked Curly.

"Alas," said Santa Claus. "This year I have only one toy engine, and a poor little lame boy has asked for that in a letter he sent to me up the chimney the other night. And I have only one toy auto, and a little boy who has no papa or mamma, and who is very poor, has asked for that. I was going to give the toys to them, but since you have met me in the woods I must grant your request, since whoever meets Santa Claus face to face, can have just what they ask of him.

"But I know the little lame boy and the other poor little boy will be much disappointed. Still it can't be helped. I will grant your wishes, Floppy and Curly, but -"

"Stop!" suddenly cried Flop Ear.

"Hold on!" exclaimed Curly Tail.

Then, somehow, into their hearts there came a feeling of sadness, and yet not so much sadness as gladness and happiness.

Howard R. Garis

"I - I guess I don't want a toy steam engine," said Flop Ear. "Give it to the lame boy."

"Good," cried Santa Claus.

"And I don't need the toy auto very much," went on Curly Tail. "Give it to the poor little boy."

"Good!" cried Santa Claus again, and then his face seemed to shine like the sun, and there seemed to be wreaths of holly and bunches of mistletoe sticking all over him, and he sprang into his sleigh, the reindeer shook their horns, making the bells jingle like anything, and then, off on top of the snowflakes rode Santa Claus, calling back:

"All right, piggie boys, I won't forget you, or any of the earth children. It will soon be Christmas, and if you don't get autos or steam engines you'll get something else," and then he vanished from sight, and Flop Ear and Curly Tail went home, wondering very much at what had happened.

And in the next story, in case the telephone man doesn't crawl through the water pipe and scare the window shutter so that it goes bang-bang all day, I'll tell you about Flop Ear and the stockings.

STORY XXX

FLOPPY AND THE STOCKINGS

"Flop Ear," said Mrs. Twistytail, the pig lady, to her son one afternoon, "I think you will have to go to the store for me now."

"All right, I'm ready to go," said Flop Ear, "only I thought Curly Tail just went, and that I could stay home and read my picture book."

"He did go," said the pig lady, "but after I sent him for the cocoanut to make the Christmas cake, I happened to remember that I needed some chocolate to make a chocolate cake, so I think you will have to go for that. I could send Baby Pinky, only she is over at Jennie Chipmunk's, playing with her dolls."

"Oh, I'll go!" said Flop Ear, and he laid aside his book, and got ready to go to the store. It was getting nearer and nearer to Christmas every day, and, though the piggie boys hadn't seen Santa Claus himself since that one time in the woods, they had seen a lot of people dressed up like him.

You know jolly old St. Nicholas lets folks do that so he won't be bothered so much when he is so busy. He has so much to do, arranging about the presents that are to go in the stockings and down the chimneys, that if he was interfered with, or talked to too much, he'd never get done.

So he allows a lot of make-believe Santa Clauses to go around the streets and in stores, making the children as happy as they can. But they are not the real ones, only make-believes, though some of them are very nice. Then the real Santa Claus has his time to himself.

And Floppy and Curly were not a bit sad that they had given up their two chief toys, as I told you in the story last night, to the poor boy and the lame boy.

Well, in a little while, not so very long, Flop Ear got to the store, and he bought the cake of chocolate for his mother.

"And here is something for yourself," said the store man to the piggie boy, and he gave him a cookie, with caraway seeds and little candies on the top.

Then Flop Ear was glad he had gone to the store, and he was walking along, nibbling on the cookie, and saving a bit for his brother and Baby Pinky, his sister, when, all at once he heard a voice say:

"Here, little piggie boy, I want you!"

He looked all around, thinking it might be the fuzzy wolf or the bad skillery-scalery alligator, but all he saw was good kind Nurse Jane Fuzzy Wuzzy.

"Oh, I beg your pardon for thinking you were some one else," said Flop Ear. "I took you for a wolf. What can I do for you?"

"I have dropped my ball of yarn, from which I was knitting a pair of mittens for Sammie Littletail," said the kind muskrat. "The ball dropped in the dirt and I can't find it. I wonder if you could?"

So Flop Ear hurried over to the rabbit house, where Nurse Jane lived; she was the only one at home that day. And, by rooting around in the dirt with his rubbery-ubbery nose, Flop

Ear soon found the ball of yarn.

"Oh, how smart you are!" exclaimed Nurse Jane. "And, as a little present to you I am going to give you a pair of stockings that I knitted myself. You can hang them up for Santa Claus on Christmas."

"Oh, thank you!" cried Flop Ear, as he took the stockings, which were very big. Far too big they were for him, but he was too polite to say so. And he thought, in case he couldn't wear them, that it was all the better to have them big for Christmas, since Santa Claus could put so much more in them.

Then Flop Ear, with the stockings, and the cake of chocolate, having helped Nurse Jane Fuzzy-Wuzzy, started for home. And on the way he passed a place where there were a lot of dried leaves, and he thought to himself:

"I'll fill one of the stockings with dried leaves and take them home. They will make a good bed for Baby Pinky's doll," and so he did fill one of the big stockings with leaves.

Then he went on a little further, carrying the one empty stocking and the one filled with leaves, which was almost as large as Flop Ear himself.

All of a sudden, as the piggie boy was going along, he came to a hole in the ground, and while he was wondering who lived there, all at once out popped a big fox, with a tail as large as a dusting brush.

"This is where I get you!" cried the fox, and he made a spring for the piggie boy. But Flop Ear was too quick for him, and away he sprang, with the big-tailed creature after him.

"Stop! Stop! Wait for me!" cried the fox.

"I can't - I haven't time," answered Flop, and on he went, faster than before. But a fox is a good racer, and soon he was almost up to the piggie. Just then Flop Ear dashed behind a big log, and there he found a little mouse sitting.

"Why are you in such a hurry?" asked the mouse.

"Because the fox is after me," replied Flop Ear, "and he is right behind me, ready to grab me."

"Squeak!" cried the mouse. "The only way to get clear from a fox is to fool him. Now what have you there besides the cake of chocolate?" asked the mouse, for he could see that plainly enough.

"A stocking full of leaves," answered Flop, "and one empty. Also part of a cookie."

"Very well," spoke the mouse. "Give me the cookie, and I will tell you how to fool the fox."

Well, Flop Ear did not want to give away his cookie, but he thought it was better to do that than to be eaten himself, so he gave the sweet little cake to the mouse, who said:

"Now, when the fox comes up here, just toss out over the log the stocking filled with leaves. The fox will think it is you, and he will carry it off to his den before he finds out his mistake. By that time you can run off home."

"But I will lose the Christmas stocking," said the piggie boy.

"It is better to lose one stocking than your life," said the mouse. "Besides, one of those stockings is big enough for any piggie boy for Christmas."

Then Flop Ear did as he was told. Just as the fox came running along, over the log the piggie boy tossed the stocking filled with leaves. The fuzzy creature grabbed it, crying out:

"Ah, this is the time I have Floppy!" and he imagined the pig was in the stocking. Without stopping to look, off to his den ran the fox with the stocking filled with leaves, and when he found out his mistake - oh wow! Wasn't he disappointed though!

But Floppy got safely home with the other stocking and the cake of chocolate and nothing else happened that night, except that Mrs. Twistytail sent the kind mouse a souvenir postal inviting him to come to the Christmas dinner.

And on the next page, provided the pussy cat draws a pail of pink lemonade from the white inkwell, and gives the rubber doll a drink, I'll tell you about the Twistytails' Christmas.

STORY XXXI

THE TWISTYTAILS' CHRISTMAS

"'Twas the night before Christmas, and all through the house, not a creature was stirring, not even - an automobile," read Curly Tail, the little piggie boy as he sat by the open fireplace in his house.

"Hold on!" cried his brother Flop Ear, "that isn't right, Curly. It should be not a mouse stirring - I know that poem."

"You're right, Floppy dear," admitted Curly Tail, "I read it wrong, but anyhow tomorrow is Christmas, and I was thinking so much about the toy automobile I want, that I guess I put one in the verse by mistake."

"All right, then I'll forgive you," said Floppy, who was sitting by the fireplace, stringing red, white and blue popcorn for Baby Pinky's rag doll's Christmas tree. "And I'm thinking of the toy steam engine I want," went on Flop Ear. "Oh! why doesn't Christmas hurry up and come?"

"That's what I want to know," put in Pinky, as she dressed her doll in her best dress, all ready for the holiday that was soon to be there.

Oh such goings on as there were in the Twistytail house! The holly with its red berries, and its prickly leaves, had been put in the windows and on the gas chandeliers had been hung the magical mystical mistletoe, with its white berries, and whoever stood under it would have to love everybody else.

And such good smells as there were coming from the kitchen! Pumpkin pies, and sour milk pudding, and apple cake, to say nothing of cornmeal lollypops with chocolate in the middle.

Mrs. Twistytail was as busy as anything, and as for Papa Twistytail, he had stayed home from the office on purpose to help decorate the house. Flop Ear and Curly Tail and Baby Pinky had written letters to Santa Claus the night before, and put them near the chimney. And, in the morning, would you believe it? those letters were gone! Yes, siree! not a trace of them left!

"Oh, goody!" cried Baby Pinky, "Santa Claus came in his reindeer sleigh and took them. Now we'll get just what we want."

Busier and busier became everything in the Twistytail house, and for that matter, there were busy times in the homes of Sammie and Susie Littletail, and Johnnie and Billy Bushytail, and the Wibblewobble duck children, and Jackie and Peetie Bow Wow, the puppy dogs. And as for Uncle Wiggily Longears, the old rabbit gentleman, who was quite rich since he found his fortune, he was so busy that he wore out two rheumatism crutches and Nurse Jane Fuzzy-Wuzzy had to gnaw him another from a broom stick, instead of a corn stalk.

Then it began to snow. Oh, how the white flakes did swirl down out of the sky, blowing here and there like feathers. They piled up in drifts, and the animal children raced through them, kicking their feet about, tossing the white flakes up in the air, falling down in the drifts and making snowballs. And the wind came down the chimney like a fairy blowing a blast on a trumpet. Oh, it was the most jolly time of all the year! Uncle Wiggily said to himself, and he ought to know, if anybody does.

"You must go to bed early this night, children," said Mrs. Twistytail after supper. "The sooner you are asleep the sooner will it be Christmas."

"We will," said Curly Tail and Flop Ear and Baby Pinky, and off they trotted, after kissing their papa and mamma good-night, their little kinky tails flopping up and down like a lady's earrings when she runs after a trolley car.

Darker and darker it grew, and still the snowflakes kept coming down until all the ground was white and the roofs of houses, too, and the gate posts and the pump in the yard and everything - all white, ready for Christmas.

"Santa Claus' reindeer can easily pull the sleigh tonight," said Baby Pinky, as she looked from the window.

"Come, get back into bed!" called Curly Tail, "or Santa Claus won't come."

It was close to midnight, and still the snow came down. Outside the Twistytail house, just as outside of every other house where the children believe in Santa Claus, there was heard the ringing of bells. Then some one called:

"Whoa, there, reindeer!"

Then there was a noise in the chimney. Maybe it was the wind, or maybe it was a little bird crawling in to get warm. I don't know. Anyway, there was a noise, but the piggie children never woke up.

And then - and then - and then - in a little while it was Christmas morning. Somewhere a horn blew. Curly Tail heard it first, and, though it was scarcely daylight, he hopped out of bed.

"Wake up!" he cried, "Wake up everybody! It's Christmas! Merry Christmas!"

"Merry Christmas!" cried Flop Ear.

"Merry Christmas!" echoed Baby Pinky, and they all rushed downstairs.

"Mercy me!" exclaimed Mrs. Twistytail, rubbing her eyes. "Christmas so soon?"

"Yes, indeed!" shouted the children. "Oh, come and see what we have!"

Well, if I were to tell you all that happened at the Twistytail house that day, and about all the presents the children got, I'm sure I would be so long finishing that you would get hungry. But oh! everything was lovely!

"I've got my toy steam engine!" cried Flop Ear.

"And I have my toy auto!" said his brother.

"Oh, I see my new doll carriage - and a new doll in it - and look at her little Christmas tree!" cried Baby Pinky! "Oh, how lovely everything is!"

"Merry Christmas!" cried a voice at the door, and there stood Uncle Wiggily Longears, with a lot of bundles under his paws. "Santa Claus left these at my house by mistake," he said. "They belong here!" and there was a sled, and skates and a football, and a rocking horse, and a jumping jack, and I don't know what all.

"Merry Christmas!" cried another voice, and there stood Grandpa Squealer, the oldest pig of them all, and in his paws he had a lot of packages, and an extra one tied to his tail.

"Santa Claus left these at my house by mistake," he said, "they belong here."

And there was a blackboard and some building blocks, and a

Howard R. Garis

toy top, and toy horns, and a printing press and a phonograph, and oh! I don't know what all else besides.

"Look at my auto!" cried Curly Tail. "It goes like everything!" and he wound it up, and whizz! it went right at Uncle Wiggily.

"Hold on! Stop it! Don't let it bite me!" cried the old gentleman rabbit, and he tried to get out of the way, but he slipped on his broomstick crutch and fell down, and a piece of prickly holly fell on him and tickled him so that he sneezed.

"Look at my steam engine!" cried Flop Ear. And he started it going, and all of a sudden it darted right for Grandpa Squealer.

"Stop it! Hold it! Don't let it get me!" cried the old gentleman pig. But the engine went right at him and ran over his toe, but it didn't hurt much, because it was so little - I mean the engine was, not Grandpa Squealer's toe. But he slipped, too, and fell, and some mistletoe got tangled in his paws, but that only made everybody the more happy.

"Merry Christmas!" cried Uncle Wiggily.

"Merry Christmas!" grunted Grandpa Squealer, and Mr. and Mrs. Twistytail and the children. And from the outside the house all their animal friends shouted the happy words, and the horns blew, and the bells rang, and it was Christmas at last.

And so to one and all of you, children and big folks, I wish you a Merry Christmas, ten thousand million of them, and one more for good luck, and may you all be happy! And Uncle Wiggily says the same thing.

So now, as there are as many stories in this book as it can hold, even with pinching and squeezing, if I tell you any more they will have to be printed in another book. And the name of that will be: "Bedtime Stories; Toodle and Noodle Flat-tail."

The stories will be about some funny little beaver boys, and the queer things they did. Uncle Wiggily will be in that book, too, and so will many more of your animal friends, not forgetting Grandpa Whacker, the oldest beaver of them all.

So, until those stories are ready, which will be next season, I'll bid you all good-bye!

Choose from Thousands of 1stWorldLibrary Classics By

Adolphus WilliamWard
Aesop
Agatha Christie
Alexander Aaronsohn
Alexander Kielland
Alexandre Dumas
Alfred Gatty
Alfred Ollivant
Alice Duer Miller
Alice Turner Curtis
Alice Dunbar
Ambrose Bierce
Amelia E. Barr
Andrew Lang
Andrew McFarland Davis
Anna Sewell
Annie Besant
Annie Hamilton Donnell
Annie Payson Call
Anton Chekhov
Arnold Bennett
Arthur Conan Doyle
Arthur Ransome
Atticus
B. M. Bower
Basil King
Bayard Taylor
Ben Macomber
Booth Tarkington
Bram Stoker
C. Collodi
C. E. Orr
C. M. Ingleby
Carolyn Wells
Catherine Parr Traill
Charles A. Eastman
Charles Dickens
Charles Dudley Warner
Charles Farrar Browne
Charles Ives
Charles Kingsley
Charles Lathrop Pack
Charles Whibley
Charles Willing Beale
Charlotte M. Braeme
Charlotte M.Yonge
Clair W. Hayes
Clarence Day Jr.
Clarence E. Mulford

Clemence Housman
Confucius
Cornelis DeWitt Wilcox
Cyril Burleigh
D. H. Lawrence
Daniel Defoe
David Garnett
Don Carlos Janes
Donald Keyhole
Dorothy Kilner
Dougan Clark
E. Nesbit
E.P.Roe
E. Phillips Oppenheim
Edgar Allan Poe
Edgar Rice Burroughs
Edith Wharton
Edward J. O'Biren
John Cournos
Edwin L. Arnold
Eleanor Atkins
Elizabeth Cleghorn
Gaskell
Elizabeth Von Arnim
Ellem Key
Emily Dickinson
Erasmus W. Jones
Ernie Howard Pie
Ethel Turner
Ethel Watts Mumford
Eugenie Foa
Eugene Wood
Evelyn Everett-Green
Everard Cotes
F. J. Cross
Federick Austin Ogg
Ferdinand Ossendowski
Francis Bacon
Francis Darwin
Frances Hodgson Burnett
Frank Gee Patchin
Frank Harris
Frank Jewett Mather
Frank L. Packard
Frederick Trevor Hill
Frederick Winslow Taylor
Friedrich Kerst
Friedrich Nietzsche
Fyodor Dostoyevsky

Gabrielle E. Jackson
Garrett P. Serviss
Gaston Leroux
George Ade
Geroge Bernard Shaw
George Ebers
George Eliot
George MacDonald
George Orwell
George Tucker
George W. Cable
George Wharton James
Gertrude Atherton
Grace E. King
Grant Allen
Guillermo A. Sherwell
Gulielma Zollinger
Gustav Flaubert
H. A. Cody
H. B. Irving
H. G. Wells
H. H. Munro
H. Irving Hancock
H. Rider Haggard
H. W. C. Davis
Hamilton Wright Mabie
Hans Christian Andersen
Harold Avery
Harold McGrath
Harriet Beecher Stowe
Harry Houidini
Helent Hunt Jackson
Helen Nicolay
Hendy David Thoreau
Henrik Ibsen
Henry Adams
Henry Ford
Henry Frost
Henry James
Henry Jones Ford
Henry Seton Merriman
Henry Wadsworth
Longfellow
Henry W Longfellow
Herbert A. Giles
Herbert N. Casson
Herman Hesse
Homer
Honore De Balzac

Horace Walpole
Horatio Alger, Jr.
Howard Pyle
Howard R. Garis
Hugh Lofting
Hugh Walpole
Humphry Ward
Ian Maclaren
Israel Abrahams
J.G.Austin
J. Henri Fabre
J. M. Barrie
J. Macdonald Oxley
J. S. Knowles
J. Storer Clouston
Jack London
Jacob Abbott
James Allen
James Lane Allen
James Andrews
James Baldwin
James DeMille
James Joyce
James Oliver Curwood
James Oppenheim
James Otis
Jane Austen
Jens Peter Jacobsen
Jerome K. Jerome
John Burroughs
John F. Kennedy
John Gay
John Glasworthy
John Habberton
John Joy Bell
John Milton
John Philip Sousa
Jonathan Swift
Joseph Carey
Joseph Conrad
Joseph Jacobs
Julian Hawthrone
Julies Vernes
Justin Huntly McCarthy
Kakuzo Okakura
Kenneth Grahame
Kate Langley Bosher
L. A. Abbot
L. T. Meade
L. Frank Baum
Laura Lee Hope

Laurence Housman
Leo Tolstoy
Leonid Andreyev
Lewis Carroll
Lilian Bell
Lloyd Osbourne
Louis Tracy
Louisa May Alcott
Lucy Fitch Perkins
Lucy Maud Montgomery
Lydia Miller Middleton
Lyndon Orr
M. H. Adams
Margaret E. Sangster
Margaret Vandercook
Maria Edgeworth
Maria Thompson Daviess
Mariano Azuela
Marion Polk Angellotti
Mark Overton
Mark Twain
Mary Austin
Mary Cole
Mary Rowlandson
Mary Wollstonecraft
Shelley
Max Beerbohm
Myra Kelly
Nathaniel Hawthrone
O. F. Walton
Oscar Wilde
Owen Johnson
P.G.Wodehouse
Paul and Mable Thorn
Paul G. Tomlinson
Paul Severing
Peter B. Kyne
Plato
R. Derby Holmes
R. L. Stevenson
Rabindranath Tagore
Rahul Alvares
Ralph Waldo Emmerson
Rene Descartes
Rex E. Beach
Richard Harding Davis
Richard Jefferies
Robert Barr
Robert Frost
Robert Gordon Anderson
Robert L. Drake

Robert Lansing
Robert Michael Ballantyne
Robert W. Chambers
Rosa Nouchette Carey
Ross Kay
Rudyard Kipling
Samuel B. Allison
Samuel Hopkins Adams
Sarah Bernhardt
Selma Lagerlof
Sherwood Anderson
Sigmund Freud
Standish O'Grady
Stanley Weyman
Stella Benson
Stephen Crane
Stewart Edward White
Stijn Streuvels
Swami Abhedananda
Swami Parmananda
T. S. Ackland
The Princess Der Ling
Thomas A. Janvier
Thomas A Kempis
Thomas Anderton
Thomas Bailey Aldrich
Thomas Bulfinch
Thomas De Quincey
Thomas H. Huxley
Thomas Hardy
Thomas More
Thornton W. Burgess
U. S. Grant
Valentine Williams
Victor Appleton
Virginia Woolf
Walter Scott
Washington Irving
Wilbur Lawton
Wilkie Collins
Willa Cather
Willard F. Baker
William Makepeace
Thackeray
William W. Walter
Winston Churchill
Yei Theodora Ozaki
Young E. Allison
Zane Grey

Lightning Source UK Ltd.
Milton Keynes UK
UKHW010229111022
410252UK00003B/76/J